# Cut Him Out in Little Stars

## SHEILA AULD

## Biscuit Publishing

First published in Great Britain 2007
Copyright © 2007 by Sheila Auld
The moral right of the author has been asserted

Biscuit Publishing Ltd., PO Box 123, Washington
Newcastle upon Tyne, NE37 2YW

ISBN 978-1-903914-31-1

Printed in Great Britain by Jasprint Ltd, Washington, UK

www.biscuitpublishing.com

This autobiographical novel is, of course, based on the
author's own experiences. However, to respect the privacy
and identities of others, some of its characters are conflated
representations of several people while others are a
representation of particular individuals.

# Foreword

I first met Sheila when she was doing the MA in Creative Writing and she showed me some of her work in progress. I was struck, not just by the extraordinary story of her missing husband, but by her wonderful poetic prose. I encouraged her to carry on, and she came to read an extract at The Blue Room – a live literature venue in Newcastle upon Tyne that I helped to run.

Time passed, and we lost touch for a while. When we met again at a book launch, she told me Biscuit were going to publish her now completed work. I was so pleased, not every promising writer manages to pull off the finished piece. When Sheila asked me to add a foreword I was delighted to agree.

Having experienced the sudden terrible loss of my own husband, all that Sheila describes is immediately recognisable to me, but it will be to anyone, whatever their circumstances. That is the skill of a good writer. Death and loss are difficult things to write about and she does it with a deft touch, full of love and humour, plus she makes it a page-turning mystery that hooks us in and keeps us reading. Sheila also interweaves the story of her husband with descriptions of her past; the richness and warmth of her time in Lebanon make a wonderful counterpoint to the cold northern landscape of her search for Len.

Sheila is a woman who grabs life with both hands; her joie de vivre is infectious but it is also the foundation of her strength to survive. She is an inspiration.

**Ellen Phethean**

For Len

"When he shall die,
take him and cut him out in little stars,
and he will make the face of heaven so fine
that all the world will be in love with night."

Romeo and Juliet, Act III Sc.2

# Cut Him Out in Little Stars

# Part 1

*'Hide me from the radiant sun'*

I finish speaking.

I stand and wait.  I know that they think I'm about to panic.  Perhaps I am.

'We'll just take a few details.'  Their pencils are ready to take down notes.

'Can you describe him for us?'

I try to describe him but it is so difficult.  The fear I feel threatens to swamp me.  I want to tell them the things I most love about him.  How he would stand and call me to him and I would hold him close, my arms under his coat so that I could feel the warmth of him.  This isn't what they want to know.

'He has a small bald spot,' I mutter, 'like a monk.'

'What colour are his eyes?'

The questions continue.  But I cannot answer.

'Blue – no brown,' and now the panic threatens to engulf me.

'I don't know the colour of his eyes. I mean I can't remember.' My knees have begun to shake. How is it suddenly I do not know the colour of his eyes when I have looked in them so often?

'Sit down love. Have a cup of tea. Relax!' Their faces are sympathetic but they want to go on asking questions, ferret out the details, so no doubt they can continue discussing and gossiping through the night. They are glad of something that breaks up their long evening.

I refuse their tea but anyway they reheat the kettle and make more for themselves.

I watch as though hypnotised as the steam rises from their mugs, and I listen to the tap-tap of spoons as they stir in the sugar.

'Now when did you last see him?' They resume the questioning, looking content and comfortable as they sip the hot drinks. One of them begins to sharpen the tip of his pencil, though it is already as fine as a needle point. The rhythm of the blade on lead becomes just another part of this bizarre nightmare.

I know by now that they are not going to rush out, jump into their cars and search for Len. They are not going to put out a call and ask others to look for him. They are probably going to sit in their little warm building, for a short while, then lock up, call into headquarters and go home to their wives.

I have come through a dark and foggy night, a fine drizzle coating everything like hoar frost, to tell them of my concern.

'How long has he been missing?' I hear yet another question. I know my answer will confirm their belief that I am panicking prematurely.

14

'Not very long then dear – I'm afraid he has to be missing a bit longer than that before he can be registered as a missing person.'

I must get out of here, away from these uniforms and the smell of the calor-gas heater. I may have made a mistake. Outside I feel trapped in a thick, dull world where nothing and no one communicates. People pass me like apparitions, wrapped in clothing in which they lose their identity, heads covered and bowed against the weather. Are they real people? Am I invisible? I concentrate on moving forward. He may be at home now. My steps through the February evening get quicker and quicker but I know when I enter the street that he will not be there. No figure at the window waiting to rush to open the door and gather me to him. The cold has entered every part of me and I shiver uncontrollably. I take deep breaths of air as I let myself in and the children gather round me with set but questioning faces.

I feel the roughness of my mother's skirt as I clutch it, peering round to see who is standing in the doorway. A woman, much like my mother in appearance, and beside her a small child uncannily like myself, except somehow more solid.

'Say hello, this is your cousin Pauline, and this is your aunt Elsie. She's my sister.' My mother is hugging this woman and drawing her into our kitchen. Mother says they've come from Manchester.

'The war is nearly over and we are all going to start a new life together,' is what she says.

There is another cousin, Hazel, already chattering with my sister, Elsie.

'She's got white hair,' I say in disbelief. Her blonde hair is a contrast to my own, that my mother says is blue-black.

'Cup of tea, Elsie?' Mum says. Both Elsies look up and nod. It's going to be very muddling having two Elsies in one house.

'Where's their daddy?' I ask. Mother doesn't hear. She is busy pouring tea by now and listening to her sister.

'My dad's in the Air Force,' a small voice, gruff but proud, informs me. 'Where's your dad?'

I am quiet and I am shy but I manage to answer, as I have heard so often.

'He'll be here soon. He's got a very important job, keeping England's sewers moving.'

Then after a little while Dad comes in. He always smells of diesel oil and soap, sometimes mixed with sweat. He sweeps Mum's sister off her feet and she shrieks, 'Put me down you daft 'ap'orth.' I wish he would do that to me but he is too pre-occupied with the grown-ups and I have to be content with a 'How's my girl then?'

Even so I am pleased to have a dad around and look smugly across at this small cousin of mine. She hasn't even noticed, but is climbing up to the table as though she has lived here forever. I refuse her outstretched hand when, prompted by grown-ups she offers to help me up.

'No thank you' I whisper, but am lifted up and put in place beside her. She makes a face at me. How can one small person feel so safe? I hesitate then make one back. Adults laugh with relief. We eat cake and giggle as though we have known one another always.

'Hurry up. I want to go!'

I tear a square of newspaper from the string that hangs on a nail in the toilet. I sit legs dangling and listen to the noises coming from other parts of the house. Someone knocks on the glass panel of the door again.

'Be quick, I can't hold on much longer.' Even here I can't get peace. I am a dreamer but there is nowhere to dream. I have to join the race, the constant competition and sometimes I am tired. They are all finding new talents, exciting new skills, but me, I want to sit and maybe read or just build my castles in the air. I sigh,

'I won't be long.'

'Time to go.' Mother, shouting.

'I've got a headache.' No one takes any notice, though Mum mutters something about Monday night nausea setting in again. I pick up my shoes, tap and ballet, and follow everyone out of the door.

Monday night is dancing class night. Our teacher is Madame de la Grange.

'I think she's a witch.'

'No she is not,' my wise blonde cousin disagrees with me. 'Witches have three teats.'

'What's a teat?' Pauline is interested now.

Madame is incredibly old, incredibly thin and incredibly agile. She always greets us by hammering her stick on the wooden floor of the wooden hut. I am very afraid of her. I am reminded of a film I once saw, where a piano teacher smashes a stick across the fingers of his student as she plays. My toes always curl in horror when that stick comes anywhere near me. To be truthful my toes are curled all the time.

I had thought once that they were ballerina toes because they were shaped as though I always walked on my points. But my arabesques and my pas de bas prove otherwise. I, like all the others, bathe them lavishly in meths because that's what Mother and Aunt had heard dancers do. It works for the others, especially my sister who can spend hours on her points.

Our dancing takes us through dark evenings walking beside prams piled high with costumes, sandwiches and drinks, to entertain in village halls, scout huts, and homes where old people receive us with hugs, because we break the monotony of their waiting lives.

'Oh she dances like a little fairy,' this of my sister.

'Never mind dear, it's just puppy fat,' to me.

A million sequins Mother sews upon our garish stiff net dresses, and then I forget that I am unable to be graceful, but just feel exquisite.

Afterwards I sit with everyone at home, enjoying the warmth of the kitchen and of the extended family, eating jacket potatoes, with never a thought of puppy fat. The wireless fills me with delicious horror while we listen to Jamaica Inn and I am scared to take myself to bed. The gas light pop-pops and mother scrambles for a shilling to put in the meter, but she is too late and we scream as we are plunged into darkness.

'It's alright, calm down, just stay where you are.'

But I don't know where Pauline is and I know that any minute she will jump on me, hands round my neck. My hair prickles with fear and the little bumps rise on my arms. 'Where are you?' my voice trembles.

A sudden blood-curdling scream and I am knocked to the ground. Then suddenly the lights come back on. I race for the safety of my blankets.

There is much competing in this house, yet sometimes we gang together, and we can be feared this way. We set upon a local lad who persistently bullies us.

'That's for pulling my hair.' We pull his hair.

'That's for pushing her over.' He is down on the road now.

'What's going on?' A shout from down the street. His mother.

Then 'Serves you right Bernard, you had it coming to you, now get indoors and think it over'.

We are flushed with success for days.

Auntie Elsie gets a job at the local Co-op. Mum stays at home to do the housework, look after the kids.

Pauline says, 'It's alright for your mum she stays at home while my mum has to go out to work hard at the shop all day.'

At work Auntie Elsie sits in a high box. She takes the money then she pulls a lever and the change wings its way across the counters on a high wire. When we go in she waves at us from her safe, warm little perch. She leaves the house in the morning before we go to school. She wears a neat little suit, a pert little hat and high heels. She spends a while, before she goes, putting on her lipstick and straightening her eyebrows. I suppose you might get fed up with a little box after a few long hours.

Mum is left at home looking at the pile of washing up, the dirty clothes and the never- ending pile of ironing. She sips a cup of tea in between shouting for one and another of us to, 'Come on, school will be out before you get there.' She wears a pinny tied about her waist and 'convenient' shoes.

'I know they are not glamorous, but they are convenient for running after you lot'.

I know what I'd rather do if I was grown up, and it wouldn't mean wearing a pinny and running shoes.

'My dad wears a uniform in the Air Force,' says Pauline. Thank you dad for joining the Home Guard.

My dreams continue. I tell myself that I'll be really good at the piano and make lots of money, and my handsome piano tutor will fall in love with me, when it's suggested we all take up piano lessons. But my tutor turns out to be a she and I am not talented, it seems. After school at my weekly lesson Miss Reed has a little time to enjoy my sister's well-practiced pieces first. Then it is my turn. I am hungry but no one cares, least of all Miss Reed. She settles herself with tea and cake, a little comfort for her while she has to tolerate my unpracticed fumblings on the keyboard. She sits too close to me and I cannot concentrate. I know she will begin to make sludgy noises with her cake and slurping noises with her tea. I try to avoid looking at her because I know she will have crumbs of wet cake in the corner of her mouth.

'Please don't touch me.' I almost say aloud. But she does. Her hands are on mine trying to force them on to the right keys.

'One, two, three and . . . '

'Get off.' I shout. Then, 'Sorry but...' The smell of cake and saliva is too much for me. I am sweating. I clutch my nose.

'Where's your handkerchief? Your hands should be on the keys. What on earth is going on?' She is exasperated, and me, I feel sick.

My sister knows the signs. 'She isn't well.' She suspects the worst. She is right, I vomit on the piano. Afterwards I am strangely triumphant. Then with the best chord I have ever struck I faint into the mess on the piano.

Not a pianist then.

'Who'll be May Queen this year?' I wonder. I know it won't be me.

The sun has already been shining this year.

'Look at our Sheila, as dark as a gypsy, after just one day in the sun.'

'There's Romany blood in my family,' says Nana, 'that's where she'll get it from.'

She is so proud of that fact, but no one wants a swarthy May Queen.

'Mum, it's me! I'm to be May Queen!' Blonde-haired Hazel arrives home from school with the good news. I could have worn a wig, no one thought of that.

'Stop everyone, hold it,' bellows our teacher, sounding at the end of her tether.

Tangled up in ribbons for the fourth time, I hold my breath. Will I never get it right? I am sure the teacher is about to ban me from the Maypole dancing, but no, she blames Bernard.

'Will you take notice Bernard. It's under two and over one.'

He is looking at me reproachfully. I stay quiet. This is not the time for a confession.

'Are you ready?' and we are off again. I smile sweetly at Bernard as we pass and he tries to aim a sharp kick at me but only succeeds in missing his step.

'Out Bernard.' I feel sorry for him now, but I still remain silent.

On the day, Hazel sits high on her throne in her blue satin dress. The sun excels itself and it is time to dance.

I hold my ribbon as though it is leading me, under and over, in and out, the colours whirling and weaving, a kaleidoscope of patterns folding and unfolding, and I am sorry for anyone who isn't a part of this magical carousel.

I drink ice-cold orange afterwards. I am panting with the exertion and the heat, and perspiration drips on to my white organza dress.

'All the way from Switzerland,' says Mum, 'not new, but it will fit Sheila perfectly.'

'You look just like a butterfly,' says a teacher. Dark, plump, sweating, in a limp organza dress, but a butterfly. She will never know just how she has made me feel. Where is Bernard? I look around. I might just say sorry.

'I thought the war was nearly over.' I hear Auntie Mavis from the flat upstairs come running round to our house, crying her eyes out.

'Fred's had to go down on the railway line, there's an unexploded bomb.'

'We thought so,' says Mum, 'we heard it on its way down, but then nothing.'

She is dishing out tea again.

Uncle Fred is an air raid warden. He goes round the streets shouting, 'Dowse those lights,' whenever there is a crack in the blackout curtains, and sometimes, but not very often, he has to do something dangerous, like tonight.

'I hope it doesn't go off, when it's nearly the end of the war,' says Pauline, innocently I think. 'Poor Uncle Fred'. There is a loud wail from Auntie Mavis.

'Bed time,' says Mum hastily. She drives us all ahead of her like a herdsman and his flock. 'I think it will definitely be the larder tonight.'

'The larder?' I croak. The shelves are quite wide and mum has made beds on them.

'It is the safest place,' she says, 'and it's cosy under the stairs there.'

'But I can't breathe under there,' I moan, 'and I feel like yesterday's left-overs.'

'There's plenty of air, besides which you won't breathe out here if that bomb goes off.'

I'm scared now and get down under the blankets. Then I pop back up with another frightening thought, 'What about you Mum?'

'Oh, don't you worry, they'll never get me,' she laughs.

I wonder if the war makes people a little mad, a little daring, makes people more able to take risks, or would Mum and Auntie have been like that even without a war. Nana's always saying, 'Don't talk to the Yanks. Stay in at night when there's an air raid, when the siren goes. There's no need to take risks.'

It seems to me there isn't a great risk in shouting, 'Got any gum chum,' to the Americans in uniform, especially as we usually get some, and as long as we spit it out before we get home.

Mum and Auntie Elsie don't think twice if they get the chance to have a night out.

'We'll be careful,' they giggle, as they give instructions for Dad to look after us all, on his night off.

They plaster gravy browning over each other's legs and then taking turns they stand on the table while they draw with an eyebrow pencil, a line down the back of each leg.

'That's the seam of my silk stocking,' my mum answers, when we ask why.

They are going out tonight and Auntie Elsie is in the middle of getting Mum's seams right.

'Get it straight, Elsie.'

'Who do you think's going to look at your legs?' Elsie asks.

'That's what I'd like to know,' says Dad, coming in from work. He pinches Auntie Elsie as, tongue out, she tries to get the seam straight. Her pencil shoots across mum's thigh.

'Shall we start again then?' says mum patiently. The gravy browning comes out, for the second time.

'I'll do it this time,' says Dad eagerly.

'You will not,' says Mum, 'get on with it Elsie.'

A bit later and Dad is asking for his tea.

'Hazel should be back with the pies from the Welfare, any minute.'

Dad makes some remark about there being ' no chance of gravy, then?' looking at Mum's legs.

'You could lick Lottie's legs.' Auntie says, laughing uncontrollably.

Catching the excitement, we are all chanting 'You could lick Lottie's legs,' when the door bursts open and Hazel is there. She is soaking wet from the rain and also from crying by the looks of it.

'The boys took the pies and climbed the lamp-post and hung them up there,' she sobs. I know the mums are trying not to laugh.

'We'll soon settle them,' one of them says.

They grab their coats.

'It's raining,' I say feebly, looking at their painted legs.

They don't hear but rush off in to the gathering dusk to rescue the pies. I don't go to watch them climb the lamp-post, their skirts tucked into their knickers and the local lads whistling, but I hear them well into the night, laughingly telling their story, over and over.

When they come back of course their legs are mottled and striped from the rain and their seams are blurred and smudged.

'We didn't really want to go out anyway,' they say, looking at the empty gravy -browning bottle.

So tonight, I shall not hear them stumbling and fumbling and giggling their way down the pitch black street, on their way to the local pub, with the only light coming from the criss-cross beams of the search lights.

No risks tonight. I go to sleep quickly.

'Mum drink this.' I am offered a Cupasoup. I try to rally.

'Now everything is going to be alright,' I say. 'I have told the police all about it. They are going to look for Len. We mustn't worry. He'll probably be home tonight.'

I look at Michael. His face is stony, set. He is the eldest. He lifts his shoulders, pulling up to his full six foot six. He has a habit of doing this in a crisis, as though he is ready, perhaps reluctantly but nevertheless, to take control.

'Why did he have to disappear?' he says. He finds it hard to understand.

'Well, people cope with things in different ways. Maybe this is the way that Len wants to cope with it. Maybe a few hours on his own is what he wants.'

'He will come back Mum, won't he?' The youngest one, John, is tearful. Len is like his real father. His own disappeared, or left should I say, when he was two years old. John did everything with Len, played football, learnt how to make things with wood, flew kites, went on the river, ...he's lost his father.

'Of course he's coming back.' I can't bear the look on his face. I have to say it.

'Now you get off to bed. I bet when you wake up he'll be here again.'

John reluctantly comes to me. 'Can't I stay up and wait?'

'No. Len wouldn't want that. He wants to sort things out in his own way, and we must go on, knowing that he will come back to us. Now off you go.'

He hugs me, kisses me and says, 'Love you Mum.' Then he goes off up the stairs.

'Your soup's getting cold, Mum.' Jacquie, little mother, is comforting me in practical ways.

'Drink your soup. Sit near the fire, you must be cold. I saw you shivering, Mum.' When it is time for her to go to bed, she says, 'No Mum, I'm going to stay with you here.'

'No, no, I'll be fine. You go to bed. I'll be up in a short while.'

James has said very little but I can almost hear him thinking. He wants to ask questions, I know, but he won't, because he is aware that there are no answers, so he waits and thinks. Soon he hugs me and follows the others upstairs.

Michael, all of eighteen years goes round the house, locking up, seeing to the dog, then he comes back in to me. I know that he is so angry inside.

He says, 'We'll be alright mum. You'll see.' Then he kisses me and goes off.

I am on my own now, waiting, with a feeling of fear, a premonition so deep that I cannot shake it off. I am telling them all to have faith and know that he is coming back, but me, I cannot summon the strength, . . .maybe I am too tired. I feel myself sinking.

✳

Grandpa comes through the gate. He pokes at a few acorns with his stick.

'Here you are, here's some big ones.'

I run to where he stands. Even though I am still very young I know that it will have to be me that picks them up. He is unable to. I polish their already shiny shells on my jacket sleeve. Nana has already collected lots with our help and is crossing the big lawn with them bundled up in her apron. I walk slowly after her beside Grandpa, keeping to his pace, holding myself in check.

'Go on, run ahead,' he says.

'No, I like to go slowly, then I see everything properly Grandpa.'

'Well, yes, I suppose you have a point there.'

'Mum says I'm frightened of missing something. She says that's why I never stay in bed late in the morning.'

I'm not sure I believe all I have said but it seems the right thing to say somehow. I often wonder what it must be like not to be able to run across the grass and roll down the hill. Nana does it of course, but then she does everything. Every weekend two of us children stay at Nana's house. We take turns.

'The garden looks beautiful, Grandpa.' Grandpa stands still.

'Yes, even this time of year. Your nana does a good job.' He swipes at a solitary weed with his stick, sending it flying across the flower border.

'I might buy her some new wellies for Christmas.' He grins at me. Even in winter, Nana is out there planting, weeding, pruning. Then she comes in, deposits her wellies by the back door, washes her hands and starts work again, only this time indoors. Perhaps she is trying to prove how strong she is, but I worry that she will wear out, and one day we will find her shrivelled up over-night, her strength all drained away. Before we are up in the morning we hear her shovelling away, clearing the ashes, and I wish that she would let me carry in the coal for her. 'Perhaps when you are bigger,' she says. Then she black-leads the stove. Sometimes she remembers to wear gloves to protect her hands but usually she is too busy. Twice she asks me to paint her finger nails, but they are so badly damaged that there is just a tiny scrap left to paint and they really don't look like finger nails. When I have finished she blows on them to dry them off, then wiggles them at me as though they are the most beautiful nails in the world. Then we laugh and laugh.

Sometimes when she thinks we are not looking, her face can be so sad, and when she falls asleep in her chair she covers her face with her apron, perhaps so that we don't catch her off-guard. She influences all of us with her laughter. Once she makes us laugh so much, Pauline and me, that we can't stop laughing, and are sent outside to sit on the concrete step and finish our dinner there.

Nana's garden is our adventure playground. She digs and plants and we watch and enjoy the booty created through her strenuous efforts. We sit under large rhubarb leaves eating freshly pulled raw carrots. 'Come on, you two, don't sit around all day.' We play tennis with her and ride our bikes on the large lawn that she mows in spring and summer and keeps free of leaves in the autumn, and in winter she helps us make slides and build snow-men and have colossal snowball fights.

'Nip to the back door of the pub and get me ten Woodbines and a bottle of stout, and put them under your coat on the way back.' My secret mission.

'Your nana shouldn't be sending you, you're not old enough,' says the pub landlady.

'She's ill in bed. She's strained her leg. I had to come.' I lie for her.

I tuck the Woodbines under my coat along with the stout. When I'm safely back, Nana gives me a sip of the creamy brown liquid, in a tiny glass of my own.

'That's for going. And don't tell your mother. I never ever gave my children alcohol, in their lives.' I turn to her knowing that I have a moustache of beer froth.

'Well, that was mean, Charlotte,' I say.

'Drink your beer and don't be cheeky,' she says her mouth twitching.

Nana is the one who climbs the tree to fix up a hammock for us, in which we hide when people come to call, and sometimes we shout rude things at folk believing that they won't know where our voices are coming from.

'Was it you two that shouted 'vinegar face' at Mrs Abrey, when she visited the other day?' She sucks in her cheeks. 'Don't do it again,' she says in a screwed up voice.

She climbs the ladder when the plums are ripe for picking and throws them down to us, from high in the trees. Then we watch as she makes jam and tests it, by putting a little on a saucer until it sets. Then we are allowed to taste it for her by cleaning up the saucers. It is always delicious. She picks the apples too when they begin to fall, carrying the ladder and hoisting it up into the trees. I can hardly bear to look as she sways about up there, reaching for the furthermost branches. I am relieved when it is time to pass the apples to her later in the house, as she stores them away for winter on the top shelf of the cupboards.

She is a woman of mystery. 'Now I want you all to be serious this evening. We are going to have a séance.'

'What's a séance, Nana?'

'It's when you communicate with the dead.'

I am not sure that I want to do that. Nevertheless, we are all soon seated round a table our hands just touching in a circle. The lights are put out, and Nana begins.

'Is anyone there?'

'Can we put the light on.' Pauline's voice, with a slight tremor.

'No, sh-hh. Is anyone there?'

'I need a wee.' My cousin's voice again.

No one is ever there, but there are some strange knockings that at first make my neck prickle, but afterwards I know they must have been made by someone just fooling about, at least I think they were. Nana reads the tea-cups too and I quite like that.

'Read mine, read mine.' There is always a fight to be first, but then I start looking in the cups and making out weird shapes, which I translate into a warning or a promise. Then Nana finishes her tea and turns her cup upside down on the saucer.

'Your turn to read my tea-cup now Sheila.'

'I can see money, lots of it.'

'Perhaps I'll win the pools this week.'

'I can see a tall dark man striding towards you,' I say.

'I want the future not the past,' she says wistfully. 'Let's read the cards instead.'

So we go on, making up fantasies for each other. Grandpa is always there somewhere, watching, watching. No one ever told us much about his accident, just that he fell down a pit and broke his back. I never knew him before his fall, never knew piggy backs with him or leap frog. I wonder how Nana feels about him. I wonder if she ever looks at another man. I suppose she prefers to have him this way than not at all. Though he must be a different man from the one she married. It is as though he went away one day and left another in his place, the day of the accident.

I see her struggle with the washing. 'Can we help Nana?'

'Yes, help by keeping out of the way.' She beats it on the scrubbing board and lifts the steaming wet sheets with ease, and pushes them into the wringer. Then she carries a huge tub of them into the garden and throws them over the washing-line. Then later she spits on the iron with such force that the globules bounce across the flat surface and make me wonder if perhaps she is angry about something. But if she is, she never tells us what it is that makes her so angry. Then she thumps and bangs on the ironing board until she is finished.

'My head's aching,' I say, one day.

'Sorry, but this is cathartic.'

'What's cathartic?'

'I don't really know, but someone on the wireless once said ironing could be that, if you put enough energy into it. I think it means it can get rid of all your worries and make you feel better,' and she crashes the iron back on to the stove.

'What worries do you want to get rid of Nana?' I ask.

'*My* head's aching now. Let's share an Aspro.'

She walks miles with us, cycles with us, when she has taught us how to balance, skips with us and turns the rope for hours, runs, and plays hopscotch with us, but she never ever dances with us. Saturday nights when we dance at her house, she never does. It is Grandpa with his poor crippled back hunched over who struggles to his feet and with the help of his stick teaches us all the old-time dances.

'Will you dance tonight, Nana?'

'I'm too busy.'

She always chooses then to dust the mantelpiece. She dusts and straightens all the photographs, and when we shout, 'Look at us Nana,' whirling and curtseying in our dressing-up clothes, she nods and smiles and then looks back at one particular photograph of herself, with a handsome, tall and straight soldier. Then she sits and pokes the fire or just gazes deep into its embers. Afterwards when we are already in bed we hear her helping Grandpa up the stairs.

I can't sleep. Yet now and then I think I am asleep. This is all a bad dream from which I must wake up. I doze and wake alternately, so it's no wonder that I don't know what is real and what is unreal.

I jump up thinking I have heard the telephone. I even go to it willing it to ring, but it doesn't. The house is so quiet. They are all asleep now, even the dog. I pull back the curtain and peer into the street, there is nothing but the shadows and the lamplight dulled by the heavy mist.

Morning does come after a lonely confused night. People will be getting up now, ready to enjoy their weekend. We should be preparing for our weekly shopping trip, happy to have a day off together. A worrying thought crosses my mind. We have no money, there was no pay-day this week. But I forget about it immediately. Jacquie is making coffee. A knock at the door. I don't get excited. It's not his knock. Whisperings in the hall.

I hear 'Len ... Mum'. My sister-in-law and her husband come in with worried faces.

'You should have told us.'

'No time – I didn't want to worry you, Anne,' I say vaguely.

'Let's go and look for him'; this is Ian.

'Where would we start?' I ask desperately.

'Well, think of the places he really likes to be and we'll start there.'

'But he might telephone or he might come back here.' I am scared to leave this house, this room even.

'The children will be here and Anne will stay with them.' Anne is Len's sister.

We start with the river. Len loves the river. We look at all the boats he knows by name, now and then having a word with a skipper.

'Yes, I know Len. I haven't seen him though, not for a while.' We don't really expect to see him sitting on their boats, collar up against the cold.

Len and I often walk for miles along the paths on the edge of the Tyne , watching the river traffic. Sometimes we are still wandering when the sun starts to go down and the lights come on one by one and are reflected in the water.

I feel now the same wind that would drive us into the Fish Quay cafés. I think of the times we sit eating fish and chips, listening to the rain pelting against the windows and how we rush home afterwards wanting to be in bed together, still smelling of fish and chips and knowing that that is not the most important thing.

Ian and I sit here now on this morning, sipping our coffees, trying to keep calm, not wanting to tell too many people about Len because that will make it all too believable.

'We are looking for this man.' Ian has a photograph.

'Oh, that's Len isn't it? He often comes in here but I haven't seen him for a few days.' He peers at me, 'Well, you're usually with him, aren't you dear? What's happened?'

'I want to go Ian.' I stand up, go towards the door.

We walk along the Fish Quay. We see strong looking women who have been tailing prawns all night, pulling themselves up off the ships. There is some shrieking of laughter as a fisherman calls some ribald joke after them. They look weary but still manage to make each other laugh, telling tales of the night's flirtations with the lads on board.

'He was gaggin' for it all night. But I told him to keep his claws off me. I'd have more fun with a prawn.' More laughter. 'Talking of which, my hands are raw from those bastard prawns. They don't like getting their tails off, which is more than I can say for some of those sailor boys.'

I am close enough now to see her hands infected by the pincers which have clamped on viciously when she has tried to remove the tails.

'Was there something?' I realise the voice is directed to us. They have all stopped and are looking at us with deep suspicion.

'Well go on, have you come to arrest us,' one woman's desperate voice.

'Why should we do that?' says Ian.

'You're not D.S.S then, or the police?' A woman with tattoos on her bare arms seems to be the spokeswoman. I wonder why she isn't shivering with cold.

We explain a little of why we are here. These tough, hard women who are not even fearful of arrest over their fiddle jobs, are suddenly motherly, compassionate.

'So sorry pet. We've seen no one like that.' They gather round.

'Thanks, we'll just keep looking.' I am about to cry because of their unexpected sympathy. A huge soft arm with a blue dolphin down the upper half reaches out and pulls me to a voluminous bosom. I am deluged by a strong smell of fish. Then I am released, and followed by copious good wishes, we make haste to continue the search.

A fruitless search that ends at a little inlet at Blyth. The tide is out and the small boats are tipped on their sides almost, wedged in the mud, stranded, just like me I think.

'Let's go home, Ian. He's not round here.'

Ian looks at me, 'Where is he then?'

'I don't know, but he's not here.' I close my eyes. Something is going through my mind like a photograph and I try to hang on to it. There is a picture here.

'Are you alright, Sheila?' A forest clearing, white with snow, yet dark as night. A place well-loved and yet, now, terrifying.

※

On another day like this we had seen a dead child. Brought from the water in the arms of two men. We weren't supposed to see. Mother had tried to get us to look the other way, told us to stay where we were, not to join the small crowd gathered to watch the macabre show. But we did see, a small body, white, almost blue and we heard the sobs of a distraught woman.

All that was almost forgotten on this beautiful summer's day except for Mother and Aunt's constant, 'Don't swim out too far.'

'Stay within your depth.'

'Come back in this minute.'

I can see through the heat haze, the boys swimming across to the other side of the lake. The air is so still, that now and then their voices sound clear across the water.

'I cut the time by forty-five seconds then.'

Nana shakes her head. 'They'll cut their lives by a lot more than forty-five seconds if they aren't careful.'

It is so peaceful. The family lie, some of them spread-eagled in the sunshine or chin on knees, chewing a piece of grass, gazing out across the lake. Mother sits with Aunt, their feet in the water, chatting quietly now and then. Once in a while, one of the cousins walks into the lake and swims soundlessly, hardly making a movement in the water. It is too hot to rush about playing mad games. That will come later when the day starts to cool.

We can hear the insects hurrying past. They are the only things that move with any speed. A time for dreamers to dream.

Another shout from across the lake, 'Beat that then.'

I look up. I can beat that, I am sure. Adults are dozing now. I could be the best, the champion swimmer. But I know how deep the lake is. They emptied it once, so that it was not a signpost to London in the war. What lurks beneath its depths now, ready to catch the careless swimmer? I shudder – perhaps another day.

I stand up and stretch, then wander to the water's edge.

'Do you want to take your baby brother, while I have five minutes?' Mum's voice.

I am eight years old. I take my baby brother by his tiny, soft hand, and we paddle along the edge of the water. He is unsteady, wobbling in his new-found walking. He wears a pink knitted swimsuit.

'Well, beggars can't be choosers.' My gran is always saying that.

We stop further along the bank. I sit on the edge watching my little brother trying to pick up stones from below the water. I hold my face up to the sun and close my eyes.

And how did little brother come to be hanging upside down below the water, his baby hand clutching at a few strands of grass, while I am lost in dreams skating across the lake in some world of frosty fantasy?

Then I am falling through ice and the creatures in the depths are eating into my flesh and I am screaming. No, it is not my scream, it is my mother's and in a terrible slow-motion world I watch as the baby is dragged from the water and held upside down.

'Faster,' I want to scream, but nothing comes from my frozen throat.

Then a picture that will be forever imprinted on my mind is caught and held. Mother, her face distorted with fear and little Peter upside down, a trickle of water coming from the corner of his tiny mouth. I don't want to register his skin as blue and white, like that other skin. Accusing faces stare at me. I want to say, 'I think his swimsuit has shrunk.'

The lake is dark now, a backdrop for this dreadful scene. Thick heavy trees hang over the lake suspended in this moment.

Then, a tiny cough, a big hiccup, a sob, a smile. Mother is crying and laughing at the same time. I wait alone, in my semi-static world, for the punishment I know must come.

Suddenly, like a sleepwalker I find myself seated in the crook of my mother's arm. Baby Peter, wrapped in a towel, and cuddled tightly by Nana, is nibbling a biscuit.

Then, like coming down a hillside when your ears pop, like bursting a bubble that might enclose you, suddenly everything is crystal clear once more. I look around. Hazel is combing her bright, blonde hair, Auntie is rubbing down one of the little ones with a rainbow coloured towel — bright orange raw carrots are being handed round. The colour reminds me of the orange streak in Nana's hair, where she dips her comb in cold tea every morning, and runs it through the grey at the front. My sister Elsie brings Nana's home-made bread round. It is warm from sitting in a tin in the sun. I bite into it. It tastes of yeast. I feel the dryness of flour on my upper lip. Pauline sitting next to me, her legs sticking out in front as though they are unable to bend, points to the flour moustache and giggles. The others, in their relief, in this second chance they have, all begin to laugh hysterically.

Later they come to me, the bigger ones, while the adults are packing up and the air is cooling. I know they are going to get me to swim across the lake, get me to be the champion.

'We know you could do it, and faster than the boys.' I am not as sure as they seem.

'No' I say, 'you heard what the grown-ups said. It's too dangerous. They've had enough frights for one day.' So have I. The others look relieved.

With me they try to walk in step, arms linked, a line of us across the river bank. Then like drunks we miss our step, sway and wobble this way and that, eventually falling into a screaming, laughing heap, legs in the air, rolling and bouncing all over the grass.

'They're mad of course Lottie,' my aunt says.

'Can't think where they get it from,' Mum replies.

Later that night I dream we are swimming across the lake but no one is ahead, we are swimming in perfect formation.

'Look out there,' my sister Elsie points into the fields. Horses, shining in the sunshine, gallop round the field, tossing their heads, kicking their legs in the air.

'Will I be able to have a horse one day?' I ask.

'They're expensive, but you never know.' Elsie doesn't want to dash my dreams but she is the practical one. She turns round into what will be our bedroom.

'All this space,' she waltzes round. 'Just for us.'

I know in her mind she is deciding what will go where – and I am glad that I don't have to think about it.

I climb down off the wide window ledge onto the bare boards. We are moving in next door to Nana. Dad is entitled to this house now. They are 'tied' houses.

'They go with Dad's job at the pumping station,' Mum explains.

I am nervous. There is so much that is new suddenly. Our own house, for just us.

'We'll still see the others at weekends,' says Mum.

A new school for me soon. This will mean a two mile cycle ride and two buses, as this new house is a long way from most places.

'All part of growing up,' I'm told.

I am excited, and yet apprehensive. I already miss the cousins, though they will always be a great part of our lives. Now and then the space here is almost frightening, after our crowded, safe little world. But of course, I have to grow up.

'You don't want to take that with you surely?' That was Mum as I started to shove Darling into a bag while we were packing, 'Look how scruffy she is.'

Mum was right of course. I had owned this doll Darling for many years. She was black and almost bald with small tufts of dark woolly hair over each ear. She had been a comfort to me through quite a few tearful moments. I pulled her out of the bag trying to believe I didn't care.

'That's the way. You're going to high school next term. You don't need things like that.' There is a lump in my throat now, in this new house without Darling.

'Come and look at the garden.' A shout from the bottom of the stairs.

Darling is forgotten as I gallop down the stairs and into this perfect garden, backing on to the Great Park. What a playground. I can still play, can't I? There's a garage at the end of the drive and we push our way in through the side door. Light filters in through gaps in the planking, streaks of light, with shiny particles of dust twirling and exploding in the brightness.

'Mabs and Charlie didn't believe in clearing up then,' says Dad, looking at a pile of debris at one end of the garage.

'It's all rubbish, I suppose,' says Mum, as she turns one or two things over with her foot.

'Yes, we'll soon get rid of it – one good bonfire,' says Dad. They make their way back out to explore more of the garden, but I stay behind. My eye is caught by a brilliant splash of blue and I pull out a bunch of exotic feathers. I imagine them adorning Mab's hat at Royal Ascot, or perhaps Charlie brought them back from Africa, part of some bright, stuffed, foreign bird. Mum laughs when she thinks of Mabs at Royal Ascot.

'No, she'd never go to the races, and as for Charlie going to Africa, he thought going next-door for a cup of tea was foreign.'

It doesn't matter. I wander off upstairs to sit on the floor and stroke the softness of the feathers. I had my own canary once but it died.

Mum has popped next door to borrow some milk. The windows are open on to the warm day. Suddenly, I hear raised voices.

'You'd have left me behind in Manchester if it weren't for Dad'; Mum's voice. A door closes. I can't hear any more. I don't want to. Peace settles again.

Elsie flies into the room. She is pleased and happy. She takes my two hands, pulls me up and hugs me.

'It's lovely here.' She twirls me round. I have my sister to myself. I catch her happiness.

'Tea's ready. Let's go.'

We run downstairs. They are sitting round a hastily put-together table, eating bread and strawberry jam. I can't remember there ever being just us. There are great smiles on all their faces, even little brother seems at home.

'Here bite this,' says Mum, and I do.

Strawberry jam oozes out of the side and plops onto the table. We all laugh – and I know everything will be just fine if I can only stop thinking of Darling at the bottom of a bin somewhere.

I tell the police in their little outpost that perhaps Len has gone to the hills. We love to walk in the hills, I tell them.

'Simonside is where we walk often. It's one of Len's favourite places.'

'I see dear. Well, we'll tell them to keep a look out for the car.'

'That's not enough. I want them to go out and look for him.'

'Can't do that yet, dear. We must give him time. Len is an adult. We have to believe he can take care of himself.'

'Stop calling me dear,' I want to shout.

So here I am on Sunday afternoon driving with Ian in his Mini, to Simonside.

'Let's go to the place that you keep thinking of,' he says.

'It's a long way and why should he have gone there? He had lots of favourite places.'

'At least we won't be sitting here, knowing no one is doing anything.'

The Mini finds it hard going. It is February, and there is so much snow and ice around, more and more as we start to climb to the car park that has been in my mind since Friday night.

The trees are heavy with snow and as we get higher we see the snow turn to ice. It covers every branch, every twig, like a coat of armour solid and impenetrable. Icicles hang down like blue steel daggers.

'It's so beautiful,' I hear myself saying.

' . . .but treacherous.' Ian is wrestling with the car that wants to turn sideways and slide back down the hillside. Then, its wheels catching on some gravel, it shoots forward and we turn off into the car park.

'There it is.' Like the Mini, my heart stops, then lurches forward again. The car park is cut out, a space in the tightly-packed forest. Trees so tall, enclosing the relatively small space, are shrouded in white, and in the wind, are bobbing in some weird liturgical dance. The car is there, exactly as predicted in this woman's mind.

Now I am running to the car, peering inside. It is empty – of course.

'It must have been here since Friday.' There is a lot of snow on top of the car but underneath very little. I feel elated. I have found the car. I feel desperate. Len is not here.

My mind is a tangle of thoughts. Black and frightened, bright and hopeful, dull and stagnant – one possibility after another flashes through in quick succession.

Ian is speaking to a woman about to drive out of the car park. 'Tell the police they have to come now,' I hear him say. She nods and sets off on her mission. Ian also sets off, in distress, to run to the top of the hillside calling Len's name. A blizzard has started but I stand as if invincible against Len's car. I notice sweet papers lying in a heap below the driver's window. Perhaps it was defiance from Len against a world that continually tells us how to live, how not to live.


The winter wind is biting, carrying the snow like fine needles into my face. I cannot tell if it is tears or melted snow that trickles down my cheeks until I lick my frozen mouth and taste the salt upon my tongue. I know there is only a little daylight left. I feel raw and alone. A Land-Rover pulls hurriedly into the car-park and skids to a stop. Policemen jump out and come across to me.

'You're sure this is the car then?'

'Of course.'

'Right, stay there.' They roar off in their vehicle up the hillside. 'Stay here.' Where would I go? I am becoming part of this scene, a white mantle enveloping me.

The wind has stopped for a moment. The silence is unbearable. I force myself to move stiffly to the edge of the clearing and I peer into the forest, frightened of what I might see and yet knowing somehow he is not here. The wind sweeps through the forest again making the trees groan and crack.

'Keep him safe, please keep him safe.'

The land-rover is back.

'We need more people.'

They take me in their car through the approaching night, to the police station in the village. Then they go with half a dozen more to search as best they can in blizzard conditions and in failing light. I am left with some poor anxious woman, brought in to 'look after me'.

'Shall I make you some tea?' she says.

'I don't drink tea.'

'Coffee then?'

I feel sorry for her. She tries to comfort me.

'They'll find him, don't worry.'

As I sip the coffee, I find I cannot look away from the window. I see the hills. I wait and watch the landscape disappear into a night, blacker than any I have ever known.

The small search party comes in after an eternity, in which time I have shrivelled up, grown old, it seems to me. They don't even notice, but are gentle, apologetic.

'It's impossible to search any more tonight. Conditions are too dangerous to go on. We'll start again tomorrow at first light.'

✻

Mum and Dad met here. Dad was fifteen. The noise in the place deafens me. I mouth to the young man but he doesn't understand and points towards a door. I nod and walk between huge wheels made of steel and brass, great leather straps that stretch up into the high vaulted roof above. I watch bubbles in oil, thick, yellow and blue under little glass domes. I smell oil in everything. The young man carries a rag of oily waste. He continually wipes, metal plates, steel handrails and brass, so that there is not a speck of dust in sight. The tiled floors have been mopped spotless too. I examine the young man as he walks slightly ahead of me. I think he must have wiped the oil into his hair. It is slicked back and stuck to the sides of his head. He probably always smells of oil.

The leather straps slap against each other, now and then beating out a rhythm that joins with the clanking of metal, and the thud, thud of steam and air forced through pipes. The smell, oddly enough, is clean, although I know that outside the pits are full of sewage and I have to cover my nose whenever I pass by.

A sudden silence as we enter the side room and close the heavy wooden door.

'Where's my dad?' I ask.

'He's in the boiler room. He'll be out in a minute.'

'It's warm in here,' I say. There's a small black stove glowing with heat.

I sit in the old car seat, near the fire. Dad sits there when he's on night-duty toasting his bread and cheese or nursing his mug of tea. Round the room against the walls are great wooden lockers with clasps and padlocks.

'What's inside those?' I ask the young man.

'Oh, nothing interesting,' he says, looking, and no doubt feeling, important. I bet *he* doesn't know either. There are charts and measures on the walls.

One night it poured and poured with rain and together with Nana and Grandpa we watched a marker climb, knowing there would be disaster if it reached the red line. I never knew what would have happened but felt the fear generated by the adults.

There is a picture in the corner, of a young and naked female.

'Is that yours?' I tease.

The young man who has been watching me looking around clearly feels uncomfortable. His face is quite, quite red. He sits down upon a locker.

'Cup of tea?' he asks. I shake my head.

Dad once told me 'Tommy loves to see you smile.' So I smile at him. Dad comes through the door.

'Hello there.' Then, 'Hot in here is it, Tommy?' He winks at Tommy

'I'd better get back to it,' says Tommy. I think his face will burst into flames.

'Bye Tommy,' I say.

He mutters something and disappears back into the noise. Dad laughs.

'Can I see the squirrel,' I ask

'Come on then.' We go into the shed outside that is Dad's office. Dad has rescued an injured squirrel and it jumps on to his shoulder as he goes through the door.

'Better not touch,' Dad says, 'He could give you a nasty bite.'

Instead I offer a small nut and the little creature takes it delicately between its tiny paws.

'Dad.' Elsie's voice calls.

We close the door and go back to the other room. Elsie has Dad's dinner, covered by a plate to keep it warm – just like Mum used to bring her father's meal – and then she met Dad. Perhaps Elsie and Tommy – but no, he's not good enough for her.

Tommy comes through the door, 'Hello Elsie.'

But she tosses her head and says, 'Come on, dinner's ready, and Mum's waiting.'

I try to imitate her admirable gesture but then, instead, smile, and murmur, ''Bye Tommy.'

He begins to blush again but whether at Elsie's rebuff or my goodbye, I can't tell.

Elsie pulls me quickly outside. 'Don't trust him,' she whispers, 'in fact don't trust any man.'

'Why?' I ask, but she is running ahead. I want to know what she knows but she does not tell.

'All around the orchard until you pick a crab,' says Grandma.

'What do you mean?' I ask innocently. I've sampled the fruit but not tasted the core. I'm a bit like a bud that is waiting to blossom and I am enjoying these new feelings, this new awakening. I study my body carefully in the mirror, pleased to see it growing in the right places, trying not to notice where it has grown too much. I think of myself as Eve. I practice offering but unlike Eve I do not give away. In the evenings I walk out with other girls, and we hide behind the hedge when we hear footsteps approaching.

'I know it's my dad, 'says one girl, 'he'll murder me if he finds me.'

We stay absolutely still while he passes and we are tingling from the nearness of the boys who hide with us. Then we kiss them and leave them, while we run home giggling.

'They smell like mother's milk,' says Doreen, who has a baby brother.

'Mine was more like tomatoes,' I say.

'Well, mine was just like horse manure'- this spoken by the farmer's daughter.

'That must have made you feel at home then,' I say.

We chase each other along the lane.

One evening I find myself alone with a boy.

'I'll walk you home if you like'

'You don't have to,' I answer.

But he does anyway. He tries to put his arm around me. I pull away, but still he holds my hand. It is dark when we reach my garden gate. 'Cheerio,' I say quickly.

'Hang on.' His breathing is fast and shallow. He pushes me against the wall of the house. I wish I were inside sitting near the fire with the family. His hands begin to knead my breasts. He is obviously not aware of the tenderness of a young woman's breasts.

'Ouch,' I say, 'Don't be so rough.'

'Sorry' he mutters. His hand fumbles at the hem of my skirt and starts to slide towards my thigh.

'Don't,' I say, pulling his hand away. He keeps hold of my hand with his, and after groping around with his own clothes, places my hand upon some cold, soft, flesh. He whimpers almost as though he is in pain. Suddenly the softness becomes hard. I try to draw my hand away but he is desperate now and placing his hand on top of mine he teaches me to satisfy. Then it is finished, quickly it seems to me.

'Sorry,' he says, then staggers off into the night, pulling his clothes together.

I run quietly across the grass to wipe the acrid stickiness from off my hands, then I vomit with distaste into the shrubbery. Is this what Elsie meant then?

As we friends pick our way around the orchard, we know they are waiting to steal our innocence.

'Have you done it yet?'

'Of course not, I'm waiting for my dream man.' But one night, when I ask the question, back comes the answer, 'Yes, as a matter of fact.'

One of us has given way. 'Well, what was it like?'

'I don't know what all the fuss is about.'

We want to know the details but she is evasive, nervous, perhaps a little ashamed at being first to give in. I shall go on waiting, go on avoiding the moment, until I meet the right one who deserves what I have to give.

Then, after all, I lose it on just any night, on some stage somewhere, but with the curtains closed, audience all gone and stage-lights down. I wasn't meant to be an overnight success. The smell of dust, of grease paint and raw blood overwhelms me. The harvester? Someone I've known a few short months, a trombone player in a local band, and he not even free.

I sit all night, with the cold winter pressing against the window. I cannot sleep. I listen for Len's step in the street, his gentle tap at the window. My eyes grow heavy through lack of sleep. I stand up ashamed that I should give in, even for a second, to the tiredness that threatens to engulf me.

Then in my waiting, half asleep, weeping, I think I hear him call my name. I think I see him struggling, tangled in bushes and branches. I think I hear him crying out desperately for me. I run to the window and look out, into a thick wall of grey darkness.

The snow in the hills is deep. It falls again overnight. Icicles hang from the trees and ice seems to grow over everything, like a hard cold shell settling on this world of hills. He loves these hills so dearly.

In the morning paper we read,

## 'Search For Missing Man in the Hills

Then after three long days they come to tell me that they don't think he is there. That he is probably elsewhere in the world. They even ask me if he could have run away and left me.

'Well, sometimes it happens,' one of them says patronisingly. 'How long have you been married, dear? Some men get restless after a time.'

The other policeman looks embarrassed. He coughs, 'We just wonder if perhaps he could have a lover.'

I tell them, 'The answers to your questions are, just sixteen months. It is my second marriage, and yes, he does have a lover. It is me.'

✳

Working at the hairdresser's is not a vocation for me. I am here temporarily until I am old enough to go into the Wrens. I'd have a uniform, meet the men, go abroad. But when it comes to it I don't want to leave. Jimmy and Mona are well read and I have the chance to learn from them, while I am working here. They lend me books, introduce me to the drama society. I don't get big roles but I enjoy being a member of this sometimes outrageous company.

I stand in the wings waiting to go on, dressed as a slave, in a pantomime.

'Are they really yours?' says one of the stars. I realise he is looking at my scantily-clad bosoms.

'Of course,' I say and blush so much, that when I go on stage I know people will think I have overdone the makeup.

'I'm not wearing that,' I say. I'm looking at a huge pink udder attached to the cow-suit, that cousin Pauline and I are about to don for the first time. We unstitch it, cast it aside.

'It's bad enough being the cow, without that,' I say.

What is it that makes people give me parts like this? I've got good thighs to slap, I could be principal boy. I remember being a black beetle once at some garden performance. I was younger then, just a child in fact. I am quite pleased at times like this that at least my face is covered up, no one knows who's underneath. You can forget your inhibitions then. Pauline and I practice making the cow dance, teaching it to sit cross-legged and so on. On the last night of the show the large pink udder appears coming up the beanstalk through the trap door, on Jimmy's head.

Jimmy and I make each other laugh so much. That's another reason for not leaving the salon. Most of our customers are upper-class, a lot of their names pre-fixed by Lady. But a title cannot make it so. A lot of these women are anything but lady-like. Lady S. comes in, covered in Pekinese dogs. She is fat. She attempts to bend over the basin for a hair-wash.

'Down Mimsie pet. Wait 'til Mummy's had her hair washed. You too Duchess.'

I trip on fat Tootsie who snaps at me. I know this is going to be a disaster. Lady S. snuffles and sniffs, or is it the dogs, as she tries to bend over sufficiently. Jimmy is at the cubicle door, grinning. I scowl at him.

'How are we today Lady S?' he asks. She lifts her head to answer. Water goes everywhere. More yelps from Tootsie.

'Do be careful girl,' Lady S. snarls testily, trying to get her breath.

Jimmy stifles his laughter. I continue, knowing water is pouring down the fat neck and on to the fat bosom. I finish, aim a kick at Tootsie who is about to chew my ankle, screw Lady S.'s head in a towel and before she gets her breath back go out of the cubicle.

'She's all yours,' I say to Jimmy, and I grin through the doorway as she begins to complain and I see her push him away as he tries to dab at her wet bosom.

There is such a mixture of people. As well as so-called 'Ladys' and chocolate heiresses there are the kind and generous village people and some just very wealthy people, who are lonely, and so often only want to talk.

Such a one is Lorna. She comes in with her stately old mother once a week. Lorna has taken to asking for me to do her hair. In a way we become friends but just in that place, nowhere else. I feel somehow sorry for her. She must be fifty or so, never married. Always talks about her horses. A 'horsey' woman in fact. Manly in some ways. Big hands and feet, tall and a wide girth.

'That's what horse-riding does to you,' Jimmy says, watching her stride almost clumsily to take her place in an empty cubicle.

Her Labrador has a thing about me. He lopes in, runs across and proceeds to jump up hugging me round the waist and making definite sexual advances towards me. I have to struggle to push him off.

'Well, he loves his Auntie Sheila,' Lorna says, laughing.

'You're on your own today,' I say, tucking the towel round her neck.

'Yes, Mother's away for a few days.'

'Must seem strange having the house to yourself,' I say. The house is more of a country mansion, in it own grounds.

'I'm not sure that I like being on my own. I get a bit nervous at nights.'

I can't imagine her nervous. 'Amazonian', I always think, when she comes through the door. Besides which she has her very large, very faithful dog, even if he is a bit fickle. I finish rinsing, and gather head and hair into a towel. She is looking directly at me, in the mirror. I think I know what is coming.

'I suppose you wouldn't come and stay for two nights, would you? We could go out for dinner, drink some wine and so on.' The offer is indeed tempting. I am hardup at the moment and unattached. Staying in a sumptuous house, and dinner out, would be nice. I put her under the drier, hand her the control,

'I'll have to look in the diary,' I say. I go out to consult Jimmy.

'Go on. It will be a treat for you,' he says. I go back in to Lorna and give her the thumbs up.

'You know Lorna,' I say to the local landlord, also friend, 'I'm going to stay with her a couple of nights.' He and his wife look at me a bit strangely.

'What?' I say.

'You do know she's a lesbian, don't you?'

'So what, some of my best friends are gay and lesbian.'

'Yes, and most of them are her cousins and you don't stay the night with them.' He's right. They are mostly beautiful, blonde and sandaled young men.

'She may be looking for a partner.'

'You're joking,' I say, but I know he's not.

I cycle to her house after work, and we eat together in their large and well-equipped kitchen. She waits on me, sometimes brushing my skin with hers, flirting with me when she talks. I quite like it, I decide. It's different anyway. We drink wine until quite late.

'Would you like a bath before you go to bed?' she asks.

'That would be great, thanks.'

She shows me where the bathroom is, hovers there, while I run the water, giving me bath salts, soap and towels.

'I have some wonderful body lotion you can use afterwards. I'll go and find it.'

She goes out. I close the door. Sudden panic. Does it lock? And it does. I feel a slight and incomprehensible twinge of disappointment, but lock it anyway.

Damn Jimmy. He got me into this and I bet he's laughing up his sleeve. The door handle turns.

'Yes?' I say tremulously, like some virgin who has locked herself inside a tower so that she does not have to face the monster.

'I just need to get the hotwater bottles from the cupboard.'

'O.K. I'll bring them when I come out.' I am out of the bath, my skin is tingling, my nipples erect. I know I am not lesbian so what is going on? Is it just curiosity? I have never questioned my sexuality. I am straight.

There is a time at high school, though, when I have a crush on a sixth former. She is no one special, except to me of course. I watch for her coming down the corridor, wait for her smile, sometimes a word, nothing more. Later I switch my affections to my English teacher. She takes us to act Shakespeare in the shrubbery and allows me to be a star now and then, playing the more important roles.

I play Romeo to her Juliet, and would have died with her if she'd asked me. That was all years ago and not important now. In fact not important then, for very long.

Now I cannot sleep because I'm listening for her footsteps, the opening of the door. I do dream eventually, of learning Romeo's final words and rehearsing them, sitting in the rose-garden at school. In the night I wake as the door is pushed open, I feel a heavy body next to mine, noisy breathing, something touches my neck like a cold, damp finger. I turn, not knowing what I am about to do.

'Damn you dog, get out.' I push the Labrador on to the floor.

Work is over for another day. I cycle to Lorna's, looking forward to our dinner out, but apprehensive, not wanting to hurt her in anyway.

'I've booked a table. Des will give us a lift and bring us home,' she says. Des looks after her horses.

'We'll have a sherry, then get ready and go.' She is in a fantastic mood and we laugh a lot.

Des arrives and we are soon seated at a table opposite each other, the candle-light flickering and caught, reflected in bottles and wine glasses and in heavy silver cutlery. This is an expensive place, no doubt about that. I feel a bit like a child at its first grown-up dinner. Excited, spoilt, loved, indulged. She watches me, all my movements.

'What?' I say, not embarrassed but wanting her to speak.

'You look lovely in the candlelight.'

'Yes, well it's a good light in here, as they say.'

I try to de-fuse the situation. Des takes us home at last, both of us flushed from wine and the total enjoyment of the evening.

'Come in for a whisky, Des,' Lorna says.

'Don't mind if I do,' he says.

This is my escape.

'I won't drink any more if it's alright with you,' I say, 'thank you for a lovely evening. I'll just go up to bed, now. I'm really tired.' She looks slightly disappointed for a moment, then smiles, 'O.K. See you tomorrow.'

It is Saturday tomorrow. I'm woken by a tap at the door. Lorna preceded by the dog, comes in.

'I've got coffee in my room, come in when you're ready. I have some clothes. They're too nice to get rid of but don't really fit me. You could have a look at some.'

'Thanks, I'll be in,' I say.

I put on my dressing gown and go in. She is sitting up in bed. Her pyjama bottoms are rolled down a little and she is looking at her navel.

'I've got hairs growing in my navel, Sheila, have you?'

'I have not,' I say, trying not to sound horrified. I know she is waiting for me to show her. I take the coffee from the tray.

'Where are these clothes?' I say almost brutally.

'There,' she indicates a pile. Jaeger twin-sets, expensive skirts. I feel guilty now.

'Try them on,' she says. I take hold of a beautiful mink coloured sweater, lower the dressing gown down to my waist and pull the sweater over my head.

'Perfect,' she says. 'Now this skirt.'

She brings it to me. I am conscious that I have nothing on under the dressing gown.

'Oh come on, we're all girls together,' she says.

I step into the skirt and pull it up under the dressing gown, then take the latter off.

'Good fit,' she says. 'Now try this one.' She hands me a jade green sweater. I turn my back and take off the mink sweater. I feel her large hand stroke my back.

'Your shoulders are lovely,' she says. Then I feel her hand travel round and stroke my breast. Then she has grasped me against her holding me with one arm, her hand on my breast. The other hand is moving gently to my inner thigh.

I could do this for her, I think. It wouldn't be too difficult – but it would be a lie.

She is excited now and begins to move quicker towards the time when I will not be able to say no.

But, 'No Lorna, I'm sorry, I can't.'

I grab my dressing gown and run like some released animal from the room. I gather my things hastily.

'Sorry,' I say again, as I offer my goodbye. She shrugs. She is holding the mink-coloured sweater against her face.

'You may as well take this,' she says and hands it to me.

'Thanks Lorna.' I want to hold her, comfort her, tell her it is not too late, there will be others, but I know I cannot. The dog is lying looking tragic on the floor beside her. He too has given up. I leave.

It is sad to lose her friendship. She never asks for me again, to wash her hair. I am glad in a way, but it feels wrong that just because we are unable to be lovers, we cannot still be friends.

✳

I am here under false pretences. I am not eighteen and my heart pounds as we approach the gates. Greenham Common Air Force Base. High wire fences stretch as far as I can see, and in the twilight I glimpse men in uniform with guns, patrolling the area and checking those who pass through. But I am in the safety of a bus, surrounded by women who have not questioned my age.

During the last part of the journey we make up faces with lipstick and mascara, shouting at the driver when the bus lurches over a bumpy piece of road. And finally we hear the command from our leader, 'Dowse those lights', and obediently the driver obliges. We begin to remove all our working clothes, and take down all the silks and taffetas that have been  hanging from the racks to stop them creasing before we reach our goal. But before we don our peacock feathers the driver throws on all the lights again, so that we can be clearly seen by anyone we pass outside.

We all dive beneath the seats screaming abuse at the laughing driver, who dims the lights once more. I learn this is a weekly ritual.

But at last we are all standing in the gangway of the bus, smelling of perfume, our hair perfect, our dresses uncreased, our insides bubbling with excitement.

American voices ask our leader for a pass and we are through.

'One o'clock, I leave,' shouts the driver.

'Cheerio,' shouts someone cheekily.

59

I follow the women into the officers' club. I have stepped into an American film. Plush velvet seats round alcoves line the outside of the room. Tables and chairs are placed on deep-pile carpets and at the front a highly polished dance floor and a stage on which there is a live band. We are early. There are few people here.

'There's a new lot due in tonight,' says one informed woman.

We line the bar, which is shining with neon lights and bottles full of unknown brews. I see an advertisement.

'I'll have a pink lady please.' I throw this casually to the bar man.

'Pink lady coming up ma'am.'

'He must be impressed,' I think.

The drink comes in a wide champagne glass with a long stem. I sip. It is frothy, a bit like a milk-shake. I feel sophisticated and confident in my new lemon-coloured, flocked dress. It is an H-line and terribly modern. Elsie has cut my hair off so that it is short and spiky, urchin cut they call it, just like Audrey Hepburn. I forget about my few excess pounds and join the group of girls laughing and anticipating – what?

The music is loud and the tenor sax fills my inside with some intense longing as I listen to its deep melodious notes. Tonight I am ready to fall in love.

A sudden commotion makes us all look towards the door

'Here they come, girls,' the knowing one says.

'What beautiful young men.' I am enchanted.

'Don't be fooled, they're only men, you know. It's the uniform that gets you.'

And indeed the smooth blueness of the uniform does somehow make them all look strong and upright and handsome.

I sip my drink, nervous now. A voice booms out,

'Jane Russell.' I look around for someone well-endowed. An elbow nudges me. 'He means you – you lucky woman.'

'But I'm not - ,' I begin, glancing down chestwards, my voice trailing away. A tall young man with smiling face is looking directly at me. He has curly, fair hair and the bluest of eyes.

We dance. He dances, I float. That tenor sax drones romantically and we come to a stillness on the dance-floor, emotions so high that we cannot move our limbs. We are looking deep into each other and I am in love.

On the way home I swing from the luggage rack on the bus, like some wild animal. I am chanting 'I'm in love –I'm in love.' The women are egging me on, shouting, 'Come on Jane.' I sit down suddenly, the pink ladies swirling inside me like whirling dervishes. I am last to get down from the bus. I find it difficult to fit my key into our front door – and I am really not eighteen yet.

I want my hair to be as long as hers, falling past my waist in black waves. Such a long way to go. She is crying.

'What's wrong?' I ask, but I think I already know.

'I'm pregnant, and he's due to go back next week.'

We both know that will be the end of it. I sigh, and wonder why I still come to this place. The excitement followed him back to America, and was really gone before that. His child would be pleased to see him. How strange, those first magical weeks, I never once thought there might be someone else and that she might have his child. And now he's gone.

'Bastards.' I mutter this, as though Mother is still looking over my shoulder. I walk out of there, for what can I do to comfort her? I long to see him standing in the hallway – but Joe is there. Joe is black and beautiful, but we girls have been warned.

'No dancing with them. It causes trouble. You'll be asked to leave and not come back.'

Joe can dance better than any white man. Perhaps it is the rhythm from his ancestry which pulsates in his veins. I have often longed to dance with him. I pass by, on the other side. He smiles at me, a wide gleaming smile. There are others around and I focus on my feet and walk into the dance room. I see 'The Crow', handsome and swarthy in a Mafioso, Italian sort of way, come towards me.

'Drink?' he asks confidently. Some of the girls glance my way.

'Jealous,' I think. 'The Crow'. He earns this name by making some ridiculous, loud cawing noise.

'I'm a reb' you see,' he says. I don't see. Ed was a Yankee – I don't remember a special 'call' from him.

'Is this some kind of asylum?' I ask The Crow. He just grins and hands me a drink. 'What's this?' I ask.

'Screw-driver.' He licks his lips suggestively, and motions me to drink it. I do. I am bored. I look around. Some girls are still in love, since that night. 'Pitiful,' I think. No, I do not want to be cynical. I have a lump in my throat. Does nothing last? Must I learn this lesson so early in life?

'Dance?' he speaks in monosyllables.

'Might as well.' I say.

We rock and roll fast and with utmost concentration. We are good together – but just at dancing. There will be nothing else. The music slows, he pulls me to him, his hot, wet cheek slippery against mine. I play up to the envious glances of some of the women around us.

Joe has been dancing. His black face glistens in the spot-light that moves over the dancers. We are near to him and his partner. His hand brushes mine and we catch each other's look over the shoulder of our partners. A streak of excitement sparks through my body. We dance away from each other but then I realise that he is manoeuvring his partner into position, so that again our hands touch.

I concentrate on 'The Crow', looking up at him, smiling. I move my hand from the small of his back to between his shoulders. His eyes are closed and he pushes his pelvis into mine. Suddenly, as the spotlight moves away, in the darkness someone is taking my hand and curling my fingers round a small folded piece of paper. I watch as Joe moves away again, dancing across the floor. My heart begins to pound. The music ends.

'I'm just going to powder my nose,' I say.

'O.K. lover.' He moves back to his seat, smiling at one or two females on the way.

I am locked in a toilet and I unfold the note. 'Will you dance with me? If you nod your head to me I will come and take your hand.' Fear, excitement, the knowledge that, yes, I will do this, I will nod my head – and why? Because I am bored? Because I feel defiant? Because I am furious at a world that makes some people feel that they are so much better than others? Because I have lost my first, my only true love? I swallow loudly in the small, quiet space. I flush the note down the toilet and wash my hands slowly and carefully, then I walk almost aggressively back into the music and sit down next to the poor, unsuspecting Crow.

I want to say, 'I really do not care for you, Mr.Crow.' But I stay silent and in the half-light begin to look around. Slowly and carefully I look from one to the other until, there, by the door, my eyes stop at Joe. The music is calling everyone on to the floor – a frenzy of notes. I know that in one moment Mr.Crow will want to dance. Joe is staring at me. I hesitate for just one second, then I smile and nod. Immediately Joe comes across the floor and just as The Crow begins to speak, reaches me, reaches for my hand and I am his.

Even above the music I hear a gasp, an intake of breath. I know the room is frozen into stillness except for us two, walking together on to the dance floor. And then I forget the world, for I am dancing as I have never danced before. When the music slows we melt into one, as we glide and move slowly around the floor. We do not speak for there is nothing we can say. We do not ask for a future, but tonight we dare to be together. Dare in front of those who later say, 'Don't bother coming back . . . or else. . .'

Come back? What is this place? A place of lost love, fallen women and broken hearts. But me, I have escaped the hook and I swim free.

# Part II

*'Is there no pity sitting in the clouds, that sees into the bottom of my grief?'*

It's a strange thing, despair. People handle it differently, I suppose. Some just give up, do nothing, but I am one of those who go between intense activity and inability to think or move. The intense activity is the most difficult to understand. Where does the energy come from? Where are the plans made as to what to do next?

How did I come to be in this street shopping as though everything is normal? I walk away to a quieter street as though I have just regained consciousness. I wish I could stay in the half-world where things mean nothing to me. The pain of loss sweeps over me again. I lean against a garden wall. A car pulls up. A friend of mine gets out.

'What's wrong? Let me help you.'

My lips refuse to move. He takes me into a nearby house. Another friend gives me sherry. So many friends. *'My heart aches and a drowsy numbness pains my sense,'* Keats wasn't it? I struggle to remember more. *'As though of Hemlock I have drunk,'* My mind jumps from one thing to the next. Association, I think they call it. Len wasn't on drugs – or was he? There was a time when he cut himself off from his family completely. Who knows what he was doing? He didn't talk about that time much, except that he separated from his wife. He was offered lodgings in a men's hostel and shared what sounded like appalling conditions with someone else who had fallen on hard times.

Len told me his father had died during that time. He felt immense guilt that he hadn't been there. He went to

the funeral and then suffered feelings of shame because his
clothes were shabby and he had holes in his shoes. He felt,
he said, like a down and out. I know so little about him
really. I had only known him four and a half years in all,
from beginning to end – No! I don't believe this is the end.

We are packed and ready to leave England, start a new life.
We need to get away. We are living in limbo, waiting for a
work permit to give us permission to go.

Every day my young husband goes down to the phone
box to speak to the Lebanese Embassy. Every day his
'mates' from the garage call out, 'Coming for a farewell
drink?', and he needs little persuasion before disappearing
into the Seven Stars. They reappear mid-afternoon bucking
and swaying like a team of sick horses, talking too loudly
and just wanting to sleep the rest of the day away, until
opening time comes round again.

It wouldn't be a difficulty if we weren't living with
Mum and Dad, for these last few weeks. I know it is a
temporary problem but they seem to think he is turning
into an alcoholic.

'He's a father now, he should act more responsible,'
Mum says, and I know she would like to throw his dinner
in the bin.

'It'll be O.K., Mum. He just doesn't know what to do
with all this waiting.'

I look at my happy, healthy baby, my love for him
making me feel fiercely protective towards both him and
his father.

'He's got his Nana to cuddle him, while we're here,
anyway.' And I hand him over, knowing her adoration for
him will take her mind off all else.

My mind goes back briefly over the last eighteen months, the joy of the wedding and finding I was pregnant not long after the honeymoon, and then the nightmare of the drive, the blue light flashing, the siren wailing and the pain growing more and more intense. Later, lying like an empty shell where I gave birth to not one child but two, a boy and a girl.

'Can't find any explanation for it,' the doctor says, 'no reason why you shouldn't have more anyway.'

Then the nurse, 'Calm down now,' speaking loudly to be heard over my racking sobs, 'you'll disturb my other patients.'

What had been part of me for so many months, my children, my beautiful babies were gone. And really, I cannot be sure that they were beautiful, because I did not see them.

'I want to see them,' I had said but. . .

'It's all over now. I'll give you something to help you sleep.' And she did. – and I knew everything would be fine if I could just stop thinking of Darling at the bottom of a bin somewhere.

But that was a little more than a year ago, and the doctor was right, and I did have a successful pregnancy, and I have a strong healthy son now. Meanwhile I occupy myself each day while waiting for the visas, taking leave of all the things familiar since childhood that I will no longer see. I stand in Peascod Street watching the guards march down from Windsor Castle, the band playing, the sun shining on the metal, and the red of the uniforms dazzling in the bright light. Being British amongst the tourists at a time like this always makes me emotional, but knowing we are leaving to go to a very distant, very strange country makes me even more so,

'You don't have to go,' says Mother, aware of my tears, 'let him go on his own.' She doesn't want her new grandson to go all that distance away, let alone her daughter.

'It's going to be great,' I sniff. 'I know I'll love it, and don't worry, he won't drink there when he's got to go and teach every day.'

'Well, I hope not.' Mother is sniffing now.

Every day as though it were some ritual I walk my baby round the Great Park, the park that has been my playground since I was a child. It is beautiful. Such a contrast, I am sure, to where I am going. Everything is so green, and the lake shimmers in the sun, in the rain, in the snow, like a light that no one can ever extinguish.

The permit comes. It is time to say goodbye to people now.

Grandpa asks, 'Where is it you're going?'

'Lebanon, Grandpa.'

'Why do you want to go there? It's all heat and flies and filth.'

He'd been there in the war of course. The first war. But I know better. It is a land flowing with milk and honey, full of the scent of Cedars and Eucalyptus. I've read about it in the Bible.

Then all goodbyes are said. We are strapped into the plane. Mum is out there somewhere crying, and I am in here embarrassed, as the air hostess comes to spray the cabin. I know it is because our baby, tied into his little hammock ready for take-off, needs his nappy changing.

I hold my sober and proud husband's hand and begin to smile.

I wonder if I have been here before in a former life. This first night in our very own apartment the two of us lean over the veranda. The sky is black except for the first bright stars of evening. Cicadas hum all around us. Further down the valley there is strange, unfamiliar, Arabic music, which comes to us snaking its way up the hill. The scent of pine and eucalyptus and the clear mountain air intoxicates me.

'It's so warm and it's seven-thirty on an October evening.' His voice.

'I just love it.' I say. Our baby is fast asleep, just five months old. He knows no difference between these countries so many miles apart. Arms come from behind me and hands are placed on my stomach.

'How's our little girl enjoying Lebanon?' He is so sure our next off-spring will be a girl. I am three months pregnant again.

'She'll be fine if she can cope with all the new wonders her mother is experiencing.'

The excitement I have felt since I arrived here two weeks ago engulfs me now and then and is so great that it causes the adrenalin to rush to my finger-ends leaving me positively tingling.

We have spent our first two weeks living with the principal and his wife. They have introduced us to people and have shown us around a little. Our home was new and not quite ready to move into. The principal's accommodation is within the school itself. It has given me the opportunity to get to know some staff and some students. The school is a Quaker one but students are from all over the Middle East. Princes and young people from wealthy families in Saudi, Bahrain and Kuwait arrive in limousines. They and others from nearby countries and from Lebanon itself pay to board and to be taught at this school. Some of this money provides bursaries for the poorer people who live locally. There is a great mixture of religions, and of poor and wealthy. A wonderful place for young people to be educated.

'Can I help you up with the pram?'

A young man has seen me looking perplexed as to how I will get this wayward pram up the steps to the principal's home. He is very dark and very handsome. His smile is the sort that melts the knee joints.

'That would be helpful,' I reply.

He lifts the pram up almost single-handedly.

'Thanks very much,' I murmur, trying not to show too much admiration.

'It's a pleasure, Madame.' He gives me another dazzling smile.

The principal has followed us up and he and I push the pram on to their balcony. His wife is there.

'Sheila's doing alright,' he says to his spouse. Then, looking at me, 'That was a crown prince you just got to carry the pram up for you.'

I have never been so far from home before. In fact I have to admit that I wasn't really sure where Lebanon was before I saw the job description in The Times Educational Supplement. Then of course I searched the books for information.

'Look, we could visit Byblos, Tyre and Sidon. We could go to Damascus. We could have trips to Jordan and Israel.'

But for now Beirut and Brummana are enough. I have to learn how to shop, how to use the taxis, how to bring up a baby, how to give birth in a different world. The way to learn something is to do it, Nana used to say.

Taking my courage in both hands I sally forth with the borrowed, rather difficult pram, with a mind of its own. I soon realise my baby is one of my greatest assets for getting attention and assistance. His deep blue eyes and very blonde hair means his cheek is repeatedly pinched. It is not long before he learns that a quick bite puts a stop to too much of that. Once people have stopped to admire the baby, I know that they will then talk to me. I soon get to know many of the villagers this way.

The village shops are very different from those in Peascod street in Windsor. Some of them are no more than a room set in the hillside with a shutter pulled down when closed. I learn to take my bowl along to a particular shop to have it filled with thick crusty yoghurt that is eaten with everything here.

'It's live you see, so keeps your system healthy,' I am told, though it seems to me like too much information.

Another shop sells two kinds of bread, the flat Arabic pockets of bread and the crisp baguettes, both are delicious. I get meat and fruit from another shop. Meat is a problem, joints of meat that is. We eat a lot of chicken but lamb and beef can be very tough. I learn to cook slowly instead of impatiently. Mince is good. The butcher mixes it, when asked, with parsley and mint, and it makes very good beefburgers, burgers anyway. I learn not to ask what animal it comes from. The slaughter-house is below us in the depths of the valley. When we see pigs being taken down we tell each other, and are sure to reach the butcher's early next day, in order to get the rare treat of a joint of pork. Sometimes the butchers kill the animals themselves and then if we happen to go into the 'shop', we are offered a piece of still warm, raw liver, and a glass of aniseed-tasting Arak to wash it down with. I am always too busy picking out vegetables and keeping my eye on the children to partake of this treat.

I soon learn a few words of Arabic prompted by the locals themselves, although most of them prefer to try out the

English they have learnt at our school. Some of us newly-arrived English speakers get together a small group to learn the language. My best Arabic teacher is a little mountain woman who comes to sell me vegetables every week. She speaks no English and no French, in fact only Arabic. She is determined to tell me everything that has gone on in her life since I last saw her, a week ago. I listen and nod and try hard to recognise the words. I repeat new ones when she has gone.

When I do begin to use words she has taught me people in Beirut say, 'I can tell you're from the mountains.'

I don't mind. I'm proud of my mountain Arabic.

We have other door vendors sent to us by kind village people. The milkman arrives, his large metal cans strapped to his patient donkey. He climbs our stairs leaving the patient donkey tied to our drain-pipe. With his ladle he pours milk into my jug. I try not to notice the little black specks or pieces of straw that now and then float on the top of the foamy liquid. Nor do I ask which animal the milk comes from. It's never wasted anyway, and is a change from made-up dried milk. I miss the little milkman and his donkey, when he stops coming to our door.

'He had a heart attack. Fell off his donkey.'

I never knew if he had a heart attack and fell off his donkey or fell off his donkey and had a heart attack.

Once I've mastered the ways of the village, I dare to venture down the mountain to Beirut, not without a friend of course. There is safety and self-confidence with a friend alongside. Beirut is a treasure chest. We choose to do our shopping in Arab souks, covered markets where we find gold, glistening and stuffed into tiny shop windows. Ropes of gold, bracelets of gold, pendants and rings and everything you could possibly wish for fashioned in gold. Rich materials, cloths with colours of purple and red are echoed in majestic tapestries. We stop to look, pointing at our favourites.

'The one up there, look, look.'

'Welcome, welcome. Come inside.'

'No, no thank you, no falouse, no msari, no money.'

'No problem, no worry, welcome.' His English is as bad as our Arabic. Before we know it however, we are seated like royalty and watch as exquisite rugs are rolled out before our eyes, like flying carpets ready to transport us to a magic world. Yet we are already here.

Hubbly-bubblies hang in rows waiting for lips to draw tobacco smoke through cooling water.

'Let's buy one for the men,' says my friend.

'Never mind the men. I want to have a go,' I reply.

We are ecstatic when we bargain and get a third off the price.

Men beat out rhythms as they shape ancient patterns on copper and silver. We have a moment's flirtation with the vendors of fresh crushed oranges and the Turkish coffee seller carrying a pile of tiny cups. He pours the bitter liquid by leaning over, as the coffee pot is strapped to his back. They vie for our attention. We are content and feel safer drinking from our bottled water. They shrug and move on. We bargain in the vegetable souk where colours are even brighter than the carpets, vivid jewels of oranges, peaches and cherries. I long to bite into the water melon. I am hot and beginning to wish for the coolness of the mountains.

We move quickly through the horrors of the meat souk, giggling nervously at first.

'It's like the chamber of horrors.' I say.

'I can't stand the smell.' My friend looks decidedly unwell.

We try to hurry through. It is difficult to avoid the channel, central to the alleyway. This carries blood away when the animal is killed on the spot, and blood must be drained off because certain religions decree this. Avoiding the drain we are stalked and slapped by entrails, intestines that hang from hooks and dangle like spooky curtains through which we must venture if we want to buy.

'We're not staying to buy meat then,' I say, as I chase my pale friend through and out of the meat souk.

'I doubt if I'll ever eat meat again,' she says. 'Let's go home.'

We leave behind the smells of flesh and blood, and these give way to the scent of spices and the ever-present aroma of coffee.

'That's better.' She heaves a sigh of relief and we stop to barter and to buy spices.

The hospitality of Lebanon comes into play once more. A seat in a cool corner is offered to us, fanned by a breeze from an ancient, noisy fan. Arabic coffee, sweet and strong in a tiny cup is offered with a glass of ice-cold water.

'How can we resist?' I say contentedly. We sip and chat and try to reach a price we all agree on.

The shopping done we load ourselves into a taxi shared by others.

'I'm not sitting next to the driver,' says my friend, as she realises we must go in front.

'Thanks,' I say. The driver smells of garlic and presses his knee against mine. My friend grins and chuckles to herself.

'Thanks.' I say again.

The dashboard is covered in blue beads and icons and pictures of the driver's loved ones. He constantly crosses himself, each time we turn a bend in the road, which is contradictory to why he does it, in that it makes me feel extremely nervous. He bows his head when we pass our lady in blue, in small shrines on the road side. The air is cooler as we begin the climb back up the mountain. I sigh as I start to cool down too.

'Hot.' The driver practices his English, brushing, or stroking my thigh as he changes gear.

'Hot indeed,' my friend says, nudging me and laughing out loud.

'Thanks,' I say.

The mountains change as evening approaches, dissolving from red to pink to purple then to grey. Lights come on all over the valley, each little group a little village. And down the other side of this high ridge that is my home, street lamps come on in this so beautiful city of Beirut and I watch the sun set into the sea.

I love the sea. My baby learns to walk in warm blue water. I swim, he clinging to my back and laughing as the waves splash over us. He is a water baby. He swims before he walks, crawling to the edge of a pool and rolling in, somehow managing to keep his head just above water until we fish him out, and still gurgling with delight.

We celebrate Michael's first birthday at the beach, knowing that in five days time he will no longer be an only child.

Jacquie is born in the American University Hospital in Beirut, and in true American style I am encouraged to have an epidural. It works well, but I shall always believe it was unnecessary, and I could have done it with a little gas and air as I did with Michael. A young doctor brings me a camellia every day and holds my hand while I give birth. A nurse comes not long afterwards to help me out of bed and take me for a shower.

'I've already had a shower,' I say.

'On your own?' she asks.

'Of course.'

She looks taken aback. I realise afterwards nurses get tips for the jobs they do. No jobs, no tips. I must have been considered very mean doing everything myself.

I am picked up from hospital with my new baby, and driven up the mountain, a bunch of red roses wilting in the heat through the back window of the car. I am worried that Michael will have forgotten me, having been left with his father, assisted by our next-door neighbour, but he crawls excitedly to me. I am glad he has not learnt to walk while I have been away. I would hate to miss his first steps.

We settle down to life with our two babies.

We dance here almost every night. Collect the wine and baby sitters and go to one house one night, one house the next, competing to be best cook, best dancer, best hostess. Whispered love, for we are all in love. Cheek on cheek, hearts racing with excitement. Skin bleached and tanned, hair streaked with too much sunshine. Round our necks long strings of scented jasmine whose perfume lasts through the night and into the next day, even though the flowers may shrivel up. Bare feet on cool floors, treading to soft music or pounding to dramatic sounds of local drums. Getting lost in another's eyes, emotions vibrant, deeper than I have ever known.

And always the cicadas chattering all around us. Sometimes they sing so loud we almost have to shout to hear each other speak, and I must not miss a single word. I soak up all there is to hear from teachers who philosophise, and I must sit and listen. I sometimes want to tell them what I think but if I do not listen perhaps I will not learn, and there is so much here to learn. They sit for hours, dissecting all the business of the world, sipping their wine, their coffee or their Arak. Then sometimes the laughter begins and wildness stirs. We outwit each other to be the funniest, tell the craziest tales, make each other lose control in laughter and leave each other weak and begging for an end. And then the music starts. Music I am not familiar with and yet they know it well. The power of Brahms and Beethoven floods across the valley and seeps into the mountains and I can only sit and gaze on scenes too beautiful, cursing Bach for leaving me feeling raw and utterly exposed.

I am raw it is true. Young and new. New to motherhood and new to far-off lands like Lebanon. Yet somehow I have been here centuries. Was this my ancient home? Is this the land of my hidden past? I fit here. Sometimes I believe I am too happy, too engrossed in me and mine. I forget the world. This is my world.

'I must admit, this is a different world,' I say.

'Very different,' my husband is checking we have enough wine for the evening.

'Well, for instance, I don't need to wear shoes, just nail varnish – no stockings, no tights, just bare brown legs.'

'Very nice too,' he mumbles.

The children are asleep, not tucked up but just lying sprawled out in the warmth of the mountain night. It's their father's birthday and nearly all the village it seems is coming to celebrate this evening. The scent of the mountain trees is carried on a light breeze through the veranda doors and the constant sound of cicadas comes at us from all sides.

'I want music.' I say.

Dionne Warwick begins, '*If you see me walking down the street* . . . ', I join in, turning the volume up. I imagine the sound echoing out across the valley and into the mountains for everyone to enjoy. '*Walk on by –*'. I have my usual feeling of excitement before a party.

The evening is well under way now. People have been drinking too much and dancing too close but that's how things are here.  Wives and husbands, mostly British, but not just British, we've made Lebanese friends as well.  A few single people, some away from home and wanting the comfort of a family.  We can always find an excuse to celebrate, to party.

'Our house on Saturday then.'

'Yes, but ours next week.  It's Bill's birthday.'

Tonight was our turn.

The door opens, and with a flourish the village policeman makes his entrance. In uniform of course.  His uniform is made especially for him, as are his boots.  The local cobbler makes them, knee-length and highly polished.   The policeman has a Gaucho moustache and thick dark hair, and strange, almost yellow eyes.  He limps a little and when people comment on this, he mutters something about an accident in which he rescued two children.  Others tell us he tripped in the face of an oncoming car and his leg was crushed.

At our first meeting in the village street he was, like most Arabs, open and to the point.

'I haven't seen you here before.'

'No.  We've just arrived.'

'I will come to visit you.  You are married?'

Well you'd think so wouldn't you?  I was pushing Michael in his pram and was obviously pregnant.

Since then he has made it his job to introduce us to many local people, and to stop the traffic every time we appear, to see us across the road, whether we want to go or not it seems to me.  He kisses each one of us on both cheeks, even the man of the family, making the sign of the cross on each of the babies' heads, as though he is the Greek Orthodox priest instead of the local copper.

Tonight he strides into the room full of his own importance, clutching a newspaper parcel.

'A present for the birthday host.'

'What is it, Antoun?' He smiles into my eyes.

I'm sure his white teeth flash and ting as the light catches them. In his stilted English, he says, 'Lebanese delicacy.'

'My God, an eyeball,' a voice says.

'No, no. Come,' he takes my hand and leads me to the kitchen. He begins to slice something slowly and carefully into a frying pan.

'You are beautiful tonight,' he whispers, 'when will you be my lover?'

I smile. I am used to him now, 'Get on with your cooking,' I say, and leave him cracking eggs and adding them to whatever is in the pan. I can't take him seriously. He is a cartoon figure, a character from Don Quixote.

The first plate full he brings to me, tossing his head a little to get attention. He gestures me to take it. He is breathing deeply. There is perspiration in little beads in the pores of his nose. I notice these as he moves closer to me. I avoid his eyes, people are watching. I feel embarrassed as though something has been going on, and it hasn't. I try to lighten the moment. It is hard not to giggle, he is so intense.

'Sorry, I've eaten too much already, someone else perhaps?'

He moves away disappointed. Brave, or perhaps inebriated people, accept the plates he offers and eat.

After a while, 'But what are we eating, I want to know?'

There is a pause – Antoun is struggling.

Then, 'Ah, I remember the English words now' –he focuses on me again.

'Sheepies balls,' he says triumphantly.

The local artist about to take his last mouthful turns a sickly shade of vermilion then jade, and runs for the bathroom. I, and others who were more discriminating, succumb to helpless laughter.

'You English, you do not understand Lebanese ways.' He is hurt.

Seizing his hat, he jams it on to his head and, his boots glistening, he marches from the room. We are left silent. We hadn't meant to upset him but things happen, don't they?

Just as the silence is dissolving, he appears in the room again. As though we are in a children's party-game of statues, we all freeze in to position and watch. Looking straight ahead he says, 'My gun,' and takes it from the drawer that he has left it in. Then he walks towards me. I search for something to say, while others hold their breath. Arabs have a reputation for volatile behaviour. I feel myself shaking a little nervously.

'Are you off then?' I say stupidly. Then someone stands between us, so I miss the effect of him twirling his gun, blowing down the barrel and putting it into his holster – if he ever did that, of course. Whatever he did, he has regained his composure, swings on his heels and like some injured actor flounces out.

My defender turns, 'Are you O.K?' he says.

'Well yes, though I was a bit worried there for a moment,' I try to laugh. I feel strangely comforted and protected by this strong presence.

'Let's have another drink,' says the husband as host, walking round with bottles of wine and topping up the glasses.

It's late now. I stand on the veranda. The sky is immense above the mountains, bright with stars. The music is low from inside, '*When you're weary,*' it whispers.

I am weary, unsettled somehow. The husband is asleep on the bathroom floor. Too much to drink? Too much of the 'sheepies' delicacies? He'd get up later and drag himself to bed.

A few people are reluctant to leave the party and drift, like left-over balloons round the marble floor. My defender comes outside.

'Come and dance,' he says.

I force a tired smile. Why not? I need a hero.

'Like a bridge over troubled waters.' I need a bridge.

I lean against him and he holds me, secure. The music fades away. One by one we sit on the cool marble floor. Someone starts measuring his bare feet against another's. Others pair up and do the same. My dancing partner presses his feet against mine.

His feet are brown, wide, almost square. Perfect feet. I am embarrassed at my 'hammer' toes, my narrow, long feet, yet I enjoy the sensation, the almost erotic feel.

'Sole to sole,' he says, or does he mean 'Soul to soul,' for that is how it feels to me.

I look around the room. We are alone. I am left with a man that I know almost nothing about, except that he reads books and listens to music, the sort of music I want to know about.

I begin to examine his face, avoiding his eyes. His mouth is lop-sided. I have an urge to kiss it. The wine is running through my senses, getting the better of me. I am glad of the distance between us created by legs and feet. When I do look into the green of his eyes they remind me of swimming under water, holding my breath. His fair hair is damp from the heat and little curls have formed above his ears and over his temples. I would like to reach out and touch them.

'I love you,' he says. His words are unexpected, his voice deep and strong.

I remove my feet from his, stop myself trembling, start to get up, but he is there before me and offers me a hand, then pulls me gently to him.

Then, 'I have to feed the baby,' her little cries can be heard. I go to warm a bottle.

I sit on the veranda with my daughter, in the vast velvet night, listening to the crunch of footsteps going up the hill. My mind is full of endings and beginnings and what might happen, because things do don't they?

Have I become lazy in my sadness? I find it hard to motivate myself sometimes. People say keep yourself busy, you won't have time then to indulge in deep thought which only leads to maudlin depression. It's hard, they say, to get out of a state of this kind. But I could so easily just sit, not bother to wash, or cook, or change my clothes. I understand now how people who lose everything they value can become like vagrants, unwashed, unkempt, careless in all aspects of health and hygiene. I go to run a bath. Perhaps that too is an excuse to indulge in morbid thought.

I am lazy, or perhaps I am waiting for some comfort to come from the God that so many tell me is beside me. Then hurry up God. Where are you? How can you let me suffer the pain of being rejected again. Twice in a lifetime. Why? Am I such a sinner? Is this punishment?

I lower myself into the hot water. I should wash my hair. The steam will make it look even worse than it is. Actually I bath a lot. It's a refuge. I can lock the door, close my eyes, not have to pretend to anyone. I can cry if I want to, blame the red eyes on soap. Sometimes I am conscious of my body, neglected, rejected. I'm losing my self-esteem. I need Len to tell me I am beautiful.

Friends can't help much. They don't know what to say. I can see and feel their embarrassment. Yet I am desperate for their company. What would I say if I were in their position? I don't know. It's too early to think he might be dead, too early to think he won't come back. I don't know what to think, so how could they know what to say?

This sudden separation from Len, after we have been so close, means there seems to be just half of me here, suspended in this waiting. I am lazy and I am selfish. I think only of myself. Maybe I should think of how Len felt, how he is feeling. What had Len decided after the meeting that went so dreadfully wrong? We know he went to a tile supplier nearby, a friend of his. He went to return a book he had borrowed.

The friend had told him, 'You've cracked it, Len. A well known hotelier wants you to decorate the tiles of all the hotels in his company.'

'It's too late,' Len had said. That was the last time he had been seen.

Did he run away? Did he decide that to disappear would be better for us all? Was he afraid of all the consequences of the failed meeting – or had he just gone for a short time to reflect and plan his next move – or was he dead? Would he kill himself? No, surely not my strong, capable Len. Where is he then?

Now and then I feel humiliated for some reason, as though I have boasted incessantly of my new life with Len, our factory, our renovations in the house, our family life, and now had I got my come-uppance? Again? Who plans our lives? Isn't it sadistic that I should be deserted twice? Do people laugh behind my back? 'Serves her right. She is always telling us of her perfect life, now she can feel something of what the rest of us suffer.' But twice, and this time I have nothing to blame, no other woman, no suspicion of our love at odds, for we are still deeply in love. Nothing to blame but the way of the world.

★

There's such a feeling of unrest in Beirut today. People stand in groups talking loudly and quite emotionally, or gather round cars with the doors wide open and the radios going full-blast. We try to understand the loud classical Arabic words that spill out on to the streets. Now and then the words stop and patriotic music blares out, filling the air with the Lebanese national anthem, and then the clear voice of Feyrouz, singing of the wonders of Lebanon, her much loved homeland. People in the street stop now and then to join in 'Behebbik ya Lubnan', 'I love you Lebanon.'

'What's happening?' We venture to ask an Arab who looks as though he speaks English.

'Israelis – they are fighting. You are English?'

We nod.

Suddenly a jet screams across the sky. There is silence for a moment except for Feyrouz. She is singing, 'Shutee a dinee . . . ' 'The whole world is raining.'

'I think we'll get back up the mountain – see what's going on.'

I succumb to my husband's arm guiding me towards the taxis. It seems quite a few people have the same idea. We have to wait awhile before we are able to cram ourselves into a battered Mercedes and wend our way back up to our mountain home.

We go first to collect the children from our neighbour. Her husband is a teacher too. 'We'll go up to school and find out just what's happening.' The two men go off and we wait, drinking the cool iced lemonade that she has just made, and attending to the children who are oblivious to everything except cool drinks and each other. Pat and I are both pregnant again, our babies due in October and November. Neither of us wants to leave Lebanon. When the men return they tell us, 'There's to be a curfew. We have to be off the street by six every evening.'

'There are to be no lights showing anywhere – a black-out in fact.'

'Do you mean Beirut is to be blacked out too?' I ask.

'Well, it looks that way.' I can't imagine a blacked-out Beirut, the magical sparkling of Beirut's many lights extinguished.

They continue, 'We also have to be ready to leave, with a few bags packed in case we need to make a quick getaway.'

'Why should *we* leave? It's nothing to do with the British is it?'

'Now there's a question.' The men smile knowingly at each other. Then, 'No, not really, it's Israeli against Arab. They seem to have hit Egypt.'

'So they may just fly in and hit Lebanon.' Pat says.

'Yes. You saw those jets flying over. They were Mirage fighter-bombers. Israel has a strong air force,' Bob says.

'A lot of Arabs think we are allies of the Israelis, don't they?' I ask.

'Not so much us as the Americans, but we have to be aware as well.'

We go home to black out our house and pack our emergency bags. I am somewhat nervous. There is a loft entrance above the bathroom door. It looks just like a black hole. The children are intrigued when their father is sent by me, up a ladder, to search the area.

'Nothing there but spiders and dust,' he says. 'We'll be fine.' I notice that he goes to bolt the door however.

In the village next day I talk to some of my Lebanese friends, telling them about our packed bags. '. . . though I don't quite know how we would leave. The borders seem to be closed, the airport's closed, there are no ships off-shore that I know of.'

'Don't worry. We have hiding places. We will take care of you all,' and I know I have true and trusted friends here.

This same night, when we are in bed, we hear footsteps coming up the stairs to our front door. We see the shadows of two men pass our window and climb the stairs onto our roof.

'They've got guns.' I am shaking.

'Sh-h-h.'

The footsteps, after a while, come back down the stairs, hesitate near the front of the house, then continue on down. School is still going on, though many of the children are nervous. Exams are under way. School will close in two weeks for the summer. It stays closed until October. If this 'war' continues how will the children get home? Many of them should fly, to Saudi, Bahrain, Kuwait and other Arab states.

We are given an explanation for the footsteps on our roof. A guard has been set up which pays particular attention to the more vulnerable people in the village. I am not sure I like to be labelled 'more vulnerable'.

In spite of the curfew I am beginning to enjoy this week. The school swimming pool is open to us families every day and I take full advantage of it. Usually I would go every day, just for an hour, but now I spend all day there. Jacquie and Michael are very happy there. Michael is only three, but he has been diving and swimming through and under water forever, it seems. Jacquie lowers herself in and swims gracefully around for hours on end. Michael takes his lead from the bigger boys around, trying to imitate everything they do. I am happy to sit, girth expanding daily with the expected November child, swimming or chatting to the other mums. The men join us when school is over and we lunch around the pool. The war for us is a healthy and dare I say, quite a pleasant, though restrictive time. Mountain air, fresh with the scent of pines, sunshine, less oppressive because we are above and away from the city, exercise that is so thoroughly enjoyed and the company of people surprisingly relaxed, and accepting of the situation.

The war lasts six days and then the curfew is lifted and so is the black-out. There is a rumour that the Israelis sent a message to Lebanon. 'Don't bother blacking-out, we know where you are anyway.'

I think about the sea along the coastline shining in the moonlight, and the mountains picked out in the moon's glow. Of course they could easily find Beirut, night or day.

The Six-Day War is a victory for Israel. The main Arab countries break off diplomatic relations with Washington. They are angry at America's support for Israel. Lebanon does not, however, do the same, but allows the American Embassy to continue to operate in Beirut.

Several of our friends, mainly Americans, especially those who lived in Beirut have left Lebanon. More decide to leave in the weeks after the war. They are nervous. They simply pack up and leave. Paul, who lives in Beirut is friendly with everyone. He has been donated freezers full of food and crates of booze from those who have hurried off. He decides to have a party 'for those who stayed behind'. We spend all day helping to decorate the apartment with palms and flowers. I notice there is very little furniture around. It is a South Pacific party. Sailors, Hawaian girls and boys arrive. There is an excess of garlands of scented flowers, a roast pig with an apple in its mouth (I might become a vegetarian), and bottles and bottles of alcohol. It is a wild , letting-go party. Some of us make it back up the mountain later. I am glad to. Beirut is suffocatingly hot at the moment. I pay off the baby-sitter. I open the bedroom windows wide and for a moment lean out. A dog barks in the still, nocturnal air. The mountains are silhouetted against the clear starry night sky. I am glad I am one of those 'who stayed behind'. How empty Paul's apartment will be without the decorations, but of course I remember now, his wife left him and took most of the furniture with her. He opted to stay behind.

Life is soon back to normal again, if this can be called normal. We swop the poolside for the beach, cricket is in full swing, and the endless round of lunch and dinner invitations begins again. Some of the invitations are formal and we dress up in the best we have. We visit the casino, to eat dinner, see the show, watch the wealthy gamble. We go to the Embassy for the Queen's birthday celebration. We eat caviar and smoke cigars. I like to dress up, find a new way to do my hair, show off my tanned skin, but I like it best when Lebanese friends arrive at the door and sweep us off to visit friends in the mountains.

Today is our first visit to the shepherd and his family way up on the hillside. The family are waiting to welcome us and draw us into the warm but simple house. They are a large family and have gathered up everyone for this occasion. We are led through an ante-room and down a step into the living-room of the house. The floor is covered in a large and exquisite carpet. 'From Syria,' they tell us.

The woven colours of deep red , purples and blues make me exclaim, 'It's perfect.'

'No, not perfect,' a very old man in Arab dress says, 'only God is perfect.'

He beckons a dark haired child who has been listening, 'Show her Raschid' he says.

Taking my hand, the child leads me across the room. Then he intimates to me that I should kneel. I do so and he points. There is a very obvious flaw in the pattern of the carpet.

'You will find something like that in every carpet from the Middle East, because only God is perfect,' says a young woman, in broken English.

Round the sides of this room are cushioned benches. There is no more furniture. A wood-burning fire throws out heat from one corner.

We soon leave this room and go to sit round a large table. A huge dish of very thick soup is brought in. The old grandfather seems fascinated by our blonde children and sits opposite them at the table. Michael seems to find a great fascination for him in return. I can see he is watching the old man's every move. He sees the way the spoon is picked up and used to stir the soup. He picks up his small spoon and does the same. Then the old man begins to lift his spoon to his mouth and noisily slurps up the soup. Michael watches several spoonfuls consumed and then he carefully lifts a spoonful towards his mouth. I swear the old man is watching him slyly from under his bushy white eyebrows. Then Michael gets it wrong, instead of slurping, he blows noisily. There is soup everywhere. The old man looks Michael in the eye and gives the loudest burp I have ever heard. Michael does the same.

The old man is laughing and laughing, the tears running down his face, which is getting redder and redder. I am sure he will have a heart attack.

Now the meal is over. We are back in the carpeted room. The men have brought in a low table and are teaching my husband a game of cards. He soon learns. I am sitting with the women. None of them speaks much English but we manage to understand each other. They ask me many questions about my life. The children are sleeping on the big cushions on the low benches. The door is suddenly pushed open and I look up. Standing on the step, framed in the doorway is – who? Omar Sharif? Rudolf Valentino? My mother talked about him. I imagined the romantic figure often. No, this is obviously the son of the house just back from tending the sheep. He wears a head dress which fails to hide the handsome dark features of the man. He has a cloak thrown around him, across his chest and over his shoulder. He looks tremendously powerful up there. He nods to us all, letting his cloak drop from one shoulder. I see that it is lined with sheep-skin. I wonder which lucky female belongs to this man. A small dark-skinned woman stands up. She has a long plait braided with bright ribbon. She walks across to this apparition. He hands his cloak to her, then comes down the step in order to shake our hands, kiss us no doubt on both cheeks. His small woman says a few words to him quietly. He shrugs, points to the room that we ate in. She hurries away. Where is the kiss, the fond embrace? Is that how a shepherd treats his wife? He is near me now, about to welcome me. He reaches up to kiss my cheek. It is then I realise he is actually shorter than me, thinner too. There is a strong smell of sweat and sheep. It was all an illusion. Not Rudolf Valentino at all.

Sometimes I think I have something in common with Walter Mitty. I turn back and continue talking to the women.

★

*Jacquie's story*

What do I remember most of Lebanon? I was just a child but there are pictures that I know I won't forget, and, too, the feel of things, the smells, the sounds.

The sound of roller skates on marble floors. Mum stacking the furniture against the walls so we have space to speed and dare. Other children envy us,

'Does your mother not mind you making such a mess?' as we sprinkle talcum powder on those marble floors and then in winter socks we slide from end to end of one long passageway.

Our doors are always open, to 'friends and fresh air', Mum says.

In the spring and early summer, the scent of cyclamen and bright yellow cowslips flows through open windows and into every room.

'Don't pick the cowslips,' Mum says, but it is too late and we are sad and surprised when they shrivel up and die by morning.

Our terraces of warm dark earth grow fruit trees, our own olive trees, a peach tree – and I can still feel the furry skin upon my tongue and the juice running down my chin, and still taste the heavenly sweetness.

The vines hang over our veranda with corkscrew curls and hairy tendrils and great bunches of firm dusty grapes that pop and burst inside our mouths.

We live like eagles on a mountain top. On one side the blue sea far below and on the other the hazy mountains.

Mum and Dad sometimes hug too fiercely, sometimes avoid each other's eyes, and then seem to be searching for something that is lost, or perhaps I just imagine that I noticed that. After all I was just a child. They bury oranges and champagne in the snow when we go winter sledging way up in the mountains. Mum skis even higher up than where we are, and when she comes back down to us her eyes are shining and she seems almost drunk, even before she drinks the cold and fizzy wine.

The car park walls are made of banks of snow and we climb on top to wave to Mum as she passes overhead on the swaying ski-lift. Once Michael goes up with her. He looks quite small amongst the adults and I think he's very brave and I am quite happy to be down here sledging. One day a friend and I sledge too near the car-park and fly off the edge as though on a magic carpet, landing on top of a surprised car, and tingling with cold, embarrassment and fright.

Our wild dog comes with us on picnics, chasing donkeys, chasing sheep, stealing our kebabs and at home he catches the squawking neighbours' squawking chickens. Mum gives chase and brings back the hen, smoothing the ruffled feathers, and saying 'It's just a scratch,' as a drop of blood appears on the fainting hen's neck.

And after all, they just chop their heads off and Mum shouts for us to come in, but we stay to watch them running headless round the yard. But we are used to the raw and basic rituals of death and stand and stare as a sheep is slain in the gutter and its blood runs away into the drain. Women around us shop and gossip and men continue their games of tric-trac, shouting, 'Shesh , Besh,' as they slam the counters down.

Mum's voice is angry as she pulls us away.

'I don't believe this place.' She is angry at the world and what she believes is the cruelty of people, who can slit an animal's throat and go on with life as though nothing is happening. And Mum is angry with herself and Dad I think, knowing there is something wrong, but still going on as though life is all about games and shopping.

Our teacher is a man with a cleft in his bald skull, having been left as a baby in a war somewhere, with an axe in his head. We go to eat in mountain homes. Someone beats a drum and everyone's singing and drinking and Dad is laughing, perhaps too much? And Mum is looking sad, but only for a moment.

The old woman, all in black, is dusty with flour as she spins the dough into a huge cart-wheel, then turns it on to an upside-down pan over a fire, to make great sheets of mountain bread. The warm smell of it fills the evening air. We're given strips to eat. The drum gets faster and we join in, clapping and twirling to the beat.

I remember driving through the heat. Hot sand and mirages. Roads shimmering with pools of water and of melted tar. Puddles on beaches, all vanishing as we approach, like dreams or ends of rainbows.

Plunging into the cool sea, then fizzy drinks straight from the cold-box, running with droplets like English rain, when it trickles down the window-pane.

I remember wet sand forming fairy castles, with towers and moats and delicate arches. Mum smoothing sun-tan oil on Dad's freckled back, Dad brushing Mum's waist-long hair in the sunlight. Mum and Dad together.

★

## Khaled's story.

They arrive in Lebanon like 'love's young dream'. He tall
and thin and seeming nervous at the prospect of teaching
children whose names he cannot even pronounce.

'How will I remember them if I can't even say them,'
he confides in me. I am their landlord. It is good to have
English people in my house. I like to look at her. She
always bubbles with excitement, like a new bride. She is a
new mother. They bring with them their baby son, as
blonde and blue-eyed as his father, but with the dark skin
of his mother. Her radiant happiness is blurred just
occasionally by fleeting sadness. We come to recognise this
as a memory of the twins she lost so recently. But she is
bursting with energy and eager to learn.

'Ma habe,' she greets me. She is determined to learn
the language. I encourage her.

'Ta'at a ' sanowbe,' we village men shout, as she passes.
She knows already what it means. 'Under the pine-trees?'
she says with disbelief, but very soon she learns to answer,
'Bukra bil mich-mich,', 'Tomorrow in the apricots.' Then
she laughs out loud.

Two of the British teachers go for lessons on the ski-slopes.

'Teach me what you've learnt,' she pleads, and soon
she acquires skis and goes off every week to learn to ski.
She tells me, 'Only fell down four times, this week.' She
shows me bruises. 'And they're just in the places I can
show you.' She soaks up the sun until she is browner than
any of us. She swims out too far in risky seas, competing
with the locals and coming back in, panting and breathless
and triumphant.

She loves this place as though it were her homeland, but sometimes I know she is homesick, missing her mother and other members of her family, and I long to comfort her. I climb onto the flat roof and lie on my stomach, peering over the edge to get a glimpse of her sunbathing. Once she is topless. One day she catches me there.

'Go away, you lecherous old man,' she mutters, 'Go home to your wife and children,' and I know I should.

Another time I dare to stroke her strong, smooth upper-arm. 'You have arms like a man,' I say. I cannot understand why she is angry.

'Well, that's women for you,' her husband says. 'Have a beer.'

And I do and we drink for hours into the night discussing the difficulties of understanding a woman's mind.

'Sometimes I think you give her too much freedom. We are more careful with our women. They learn to be content,' I say.

'I think she's content, happy anyway,' comes the answer. He flips another beer cap and tips the liquid into his mouth.

'You're content anyway,' I laugh.

'Certainly am. Lovely wife. Third child on the way. Sunshine and beer. What more could I ask for?' He pauses. 'You're right though. She has a sort of restlessness sometimes. I want to say, "Hey, slow down, you can't do it all at once."'

'I notice she loves to learn.' I say. 'She wants to do everything. I think she'd be in the cricket team if you would let her.'

'Hang on,' he says, 'there are limits you know.'

He is proud of his prowess on the cricket field, and indeed he is good.

'I see her watching you and when you shatter the – er – what do you call it?'

'The wicket?'

'Yes, the wicket, I can see her clapping, adoring you, like some hero.'

'Steady on,' he looks pleased. Then his face changes and he says wistfully, 'but so often she isn't there, when I look round.'

I shrug, 'Children always come first in their mother's lives. What can we do?' And I want to say, 'And you are never there to see her flying down the mountain on the ski slopes . . . perhaps you should have learned to ski.'

I wonder if it's jealousy that claws at me, when I hear them laughing and see them weak and helpless from some joke, leaning against each other, until the laughing turns into hugging, and then into a desperate and passionate embrace.

Then with their three little ones and she heavily pregnant once again, they decide that they must go back home to England. I watch them with a leaden heart. The children are excited, well of course.

'We're going to live at Nana's,' says Michael the eldest, a beaming smile on his face.

She is crying softly, allowing tears to slide unchecked down her cheeks, while she hugs this one and that one. I notice others are crying too, and I have to swallow the lump that is lodged in my throat.

'You belong here – you're safe with us,' I say, like some Eastern oracle.

'Perhaps,' he says, as he helps to ease her into a front seat. A sob escapes from her.

A little arm comes from the back and winds itself round her neck, to comfort her. She pats it gently. He shakes my hand. I kiss him on both cheeks. He seats himself behind the steering-wheel, starts the car, turns to smile at the children, then at us, pats her knee, then pointing forward, 'Wagons Ho!' he says, and they are gone.

The drains have overflowed again. I can't believe it. The kitchen floor is flooded with dirty, putrid water.

'I can't live in these conditions.' I utter a few choice words to no one in particular. No one's here luckily. 'Thank God we are going to England, where the plumbing works!'

Then 'No, no I don't mean that.'

I run on to the verandah as though out there I can hold this country in my arms to show my love for it. My vision is blurred with tears of frustration over the drain blockage, mixed with tears of sadness that we could even think about leaving here.

Of course, we are all longing to see England and especially the people there, but I am scared, fearful of being homeless, jobless and more or less penniless.

Why are we going? Mainly, I suppose, because we think it is time the children knew their grandparents, their aunts and uncles, but also the school here is not the same as when we first arrived. We are told there is a lack of funds, so that the metal-work and wood-work shops that were the pride and joy of the place when they opened, have been closed down bit by bit. Metal-work is finished and wood-work is just taught as a hobby. This isn't what my husband came here for. He set up those workshops with another Englishman. They obtained and installed the machines, then taught the subjects to 'O'level. The contracts may not be renewed anyway. It is time to go.

I should mop the kitchen floor but I lean on the balcony rail. Beirut is there below us, down the mountainside, shimmering in the heat, and the sea as a back-drop, stretches like a blue carpet to the horizon. Must we leave all this for the unknown?

It's lunch time. Their father picked the children up from school. There is no afternoon school here in the summer. I am ready with swim-suits and picnic. We are off to the beach for the afternoon. We stop on the way, to buy one or two things at Wakim's. Wakim has opened a supermarket. His is the only one in this mountain area. There are lots in England. We go to Wakim's quite often. Today he gives the children chocolate and we buy cold drinks to fill the cold-bag.

'We're leaving Lebanon in a couple of week's time,' husband says to Wakim. 'We'll be along to stock up for our journey.' He is cheerful, optimistic, but his words turn like a knife inside me.

Today we are a little extravagant and instead of going to a free beach we go to a 'paying' beach. We la out the beach mats and the beach attendant rushes to put up the sunshades, position the table, bring us sun beds. Michael is already in the sea, diving in the waves, watched closely by the beach life-saver, a hairy, brown giant, now a friend of ours, who calls to the rest of us. Jacquie is a little more cautious than the boys but goes along, holding her tall father's hand, and then swims sedately beside him. James is busy tunnelling into the sand, trying to make complicated waterways. The sun is so warm on my skin. If I were a cat I would be purring. How can we even think of leaving this?

Friends arrive, sit beside us and we pop open the ice-cold beer and the Coke. I count the children for the tenth time, friends' children as well. No matter how often I tell myself the others are not my responsibility, I still do this incessant counting.

Richard! Where's Richard? I won't panic. He's not my child. His parents must know where he is. They are chatting unperturbed. They have a lot of children. They may not have noticed. Richard is one of the older ones, he can take care of himself. I count again.

Then, 'Where's Richard?' I say in a loud voice.

'He's taken his fishing-rod to the end of the beach, on the rocks,' says his father calmly. 'You haven't been counting up again have you?' He smiles.

'Yes, I have as a matter of fact,' I say angrily.

What on earth is wrong with me? I get up, stride into the sea and throw myself under a wave. We never do anything on our own anymore. Why am I suddenly thinking like this as I swim out to sea? Might be because I heard a husband and wife planning a night out while I was obsessed with counting.

'Early night for this lot,' husband indicates with his head towards the children, dozing and quiet in the back seat of the car. We are on our way back up the mountain.

'Yes, at least they are already showered, that's one of the good things about a paying beach. So supper and bed for them, and I won't be far behind.'

'Oh, early night eh?' He grins, 'I'm all for that.'

'That wasn't quite what I was thinking,' but I squeeze his arm, lovingly.

I like the way I feel after a few hours at the beach, in the fresh air and the sun, glowing, and yet totally relaxed. We do have an early night and we don't sleep straightaway. When the passion has ebbed and we lie contentedly side by side, I take the opportunity. I say, 'Do you think we two, on our own, could go for a meal somewhere, get a baby-sitter and just us two could take ourselves off, tell no one where we are going?'

'Well, I suppose so. Why not?'

'It's just that we are always, always surrounded by others. I love them all dearly, but just for once could we do this on our own?'

I want him to understand how important this is to me.

'Could be dangerous,' he teases.

It could of course. We might not have anything to say to each other. Or we might say too much. Why do I want to do this? I ask myself the question. I lie awake trying to answer it. I doze off, then, wake suddenly —because I want to feel cherished, special, number one in his life. At parties he tells people, 'We go our own ways, as long as we come together at the end, that seems alright to me.' Once, I asked him to stay with me during a party, let everyone know I was his and loved.

He said, 'Well I'm sure they all know that,' but he stayed with me for about half the evening.

I don't want to be possessed, by any means, but somehow I want to feel he cares. I know he does care but I want to *feel* it, and I suppose I want others to *see* it. I'm just a woman after all.

It's a wonderful feeling to sit opposite him when we take ourselves off a few days later for our special dinner. It's a place in Beirut that we have never been before. I shall remember the many candles, tall and white reflected in mirrors, and waiters in black with starched white aprons, attentive but discreet.

We could be the only couple in the room. I am not aware of anyone but us. We are slightly nervous at first, as though we are on a first date, but the wine soon makes us relax and we have eyes only for each other. We can discover so much about each other, alone like this. We hold hands across the table. 'Everything will be just fine in England , you'll see,' he comforts me.

Away from this excitement, this wild, fast way of living, these many friends, and also away from these quiet mountains, these evenings humming with cicadas, watching the sun go down changing the colours, like the film of bubbles bursting on the mountain tops, will everything be fine? Going home to my family waiting in England with open arms and friends queuing up to meet us again. The park too, waiting to open its delights to my children and to be revisited by myself. Will it all be fine? The mixture of feelings is almost too much for me to contemplate. So I don't, not this evening. We spend too much money, having exotic desserts and liqueurs with our coffees. We don't stop talking. We are reluctant to end the evening but we really are the only couple here now. Our waiter is patient and doesn't rush over with the bill until we look in his direction.

We walk out into the warm evening air. A perfect evening. I can smell the jasmine from the trees nearby.

'Thanks for that,' I hear the words, but then, 'Let's not go home yet, let's go to Emile's.'

Emile has a Greek restaurant-cum-night club in Beirut. We go there every week, more than once. We have many friends there. We never leave until 5.00 in the morning. We dance Greek dancing and sing Greek songs. I love it there, but not tonight. Why tonight?

He doesn't really understand or we would have gone home.

He hails a taxi. We are there in ten minutes. He goes ahead of me into the club. I hear people cheer. I follow quietly.

They joke. 'You've done what? Been for a meal on your own? Are you in love or something?'

Emile claims me for a dance. The music is soft, romantic.

'Well, if it had been me,' he says gently, 'I would definitely have taken you home to bed after that.'

I smile and rest my head on his shoulder. After a while I look up and start to count our many friends.

I begin the search. The search that makes me order a bus driver to stop – that makes me jump down from the bus and run madly through the busy street chasing him. But it is not him. I stand and sob when I realise. Passers-by skirt round me embarrassed. No one asks me what is wrong, as though I am some lunatic, escaped for a while from my carer. My grief cuts me off from the world. The searching throws me into limbo.

People come to visit me.

'Any news?' they ask.

And always I shake my head. There is nothing then to say. I am conscious now and then that they are talking to Jacquie, asking the children more questions, whispering. They hold my 'dead' hand sometimes, as though trying to warm me back into their world. I can only wait and listen and search in my mind for somewhere else to look and only do the things I'm forced to do.

I am forced to sit in a smoky hall, and listen to the angry arguments that erupt, between people who are desperate for money to feed their children, and those behind the windows who 'are only doing their jobs.'

I fill in form after form. Stupid questions from the D.S.S. Am I married? Am I widowed? Am I single? I tick all the little boxes in anger and frustration and go back to my search.

★

An Indian Summer, when the sky is empty of clou  
the trees begin to turn, to gold, to red and to orange.
Brilliant days when I sit waiting, in sunshine gentler than
that of Lebanon. The dew is heavy in the mornings and
leaves a dank and rotting scent, not unpleasant, but one
that will stay forever in my memory and remind me of that
waiting time.

Back in England now we live for a while with my patient
mother and father. I feel cocooned in their care. They
have bought bunk-beds and bicycles for the children, and
we in return have invaded their home with washing,
ironing, shopping and children. My children are the third
generation of our family to sign on at the little church
school in the nearby village. The surnames of their friends
are the same family names that I knew when I was there.
People do not all move on, move away, have exciting lives
abroad. They are content to put their roots down deep and
never tear them up.

I go to the hospital, for a check-up. This baby will be born
in Royal Ascot. Jacquie hopes for a girl, a sister.
 'In for a check-up are you?' The nurse asks.
 'Yes', I answer, slightly nervous at her tone. Travelling
overland from Lebanon to here by car may have been
exciting, but has left my legs and ankles swollen, as though
they have been blown up with a special air-pump.
 'Is something wrong?' I ask.
 'Nothing wrong, but we're keeping you in. Can you
send your mother home for your overnight things? You
are about to have a baby.'

It is eleven-thirty on a bright October morning and by four o'clock I am the mother of one more baby boy. I have always felt an immediate love for all my new-born, and John is no exception. This time the birth is as natural as Michael's , a few sniffs of gas and air, a little strong language and he is out, ready to face the world.

My mother's house is now draped in nappies, and bottles line themselves up in her fridge and on her sink. Sleep is disturbed at night. Baby's cries wake one child, one child wakes another, and soon everyone is awake. Still my mother loves us, plays with the children, reads to the children, organises endless games of hide and seek, in the house , in the park , in the garden.

I take my baby, now a few months old, to watch his brothers and sister at their first English sports day. I am trying not to show the immense pride I have in them. Michael and Jacquie are taller than other class members. Their skin is still golden-brown from unlimited sunshine. Their hair is almost white-blonde. They are so fit. I watch them winning every race they enter, and I have to tie myself down on the grassy bank, to prevent myself from jumping up and down and cheering with excitement. Then little James, dark skinned, his eyes looking almost black and his mop of dark hair sparkling in the light, lines up for his nursery class race. The spider-race, and he is off, his strong arms and legs racing down the playground leaving the others standing. James was born with a hole in his heart.

'Just a small one,' the doctor told us. 'It may close up as he gets older. Just watch him. If he becomes breathless, or faints, or doesn't seem to be growing, let us know straight away.'

He is the tallest child in his class and winning races. The head teacher looks embarrassed as he awards yet another one of our family a trophy. I suppose the young people who usually win every year must wonder at, and perhaps resent, these newcomers. We go home and party.

Of course, life isn't all balloons and streamers. Some sections of English life are difficult to cope with. Changing the clocks and plunging us into darkness at four-thirty is not enjoyed. Having to walk home from school on dark, freezing nights with tired children muffled up in hats, scarves and all the paraphernalia required to keep out the English winter. Trying to think of new ways to amuse four children on long, wet days when it is impossible to venture out.

We decide to go for riding lessons. A friend and I leave the baby with Mum and take the other three along. The riding school is warm and sheltered from the weather at this time of year. We learn to mount, trot and canter. The young ones are naturals but not so we adults. Our beasts are so large I need steps to climb on to the back of mine and even so I hang at intervals almost under the stomach of my animal, as I struggle to mount. Once on, things are never so bad and even when my horse bolts, in fear of a moving hose-pipe, I manage to hang on until he calms down.

'Nothing to it,' I say to my laughing, unsympathetic family. 'What am I doing here?' I mutter to my friend. Other occurrences are sent to ruffle my steady little world. Michael for the first time has become aware of the female element around him. Not surprising, as he comes home most days with little notes he has received from the girls in his class, all expressing love and devotion for him, and decorated in many hearts, bleeding and pricked by arrows. Then walking home from school one day, Michael says the F. word very loudly and begins to give me in explicit detail the meaning of this word. I am horrified and explain that this is not a word we use. I have never heard my children use this word or any like it in Lebanon. Is it the fault of an English school, English children or is it just part of growing up?

To celebrate Michael's ninth and Jacquie's eighth birthday we take our party into the Great Park beside the lake bright in the spring sunshine . We picnic under the trees and play wonderful ball games, running, catching and racing in the grassy open space. Emily, Jacquie's new friend, drapes herself along a tree, sighing and fluttering like some little wounded bird, trying to catch Michael's eye.

'No food for me,' she whispers.

'O.K.' I say, and she gets none. Michael as usual is in the middle of the activity, the leader of the pack, oblivious of Emily's admiration. Jacquie with a small backward glance at Emily, runs to join in, and James like a little bull-terrier snaps at their heels.

Emily after a few more wistful sighs realises attention is not forthcoming, admits defeat and, reluctantly at first, joins the game and later the eating.

I am glad that I can introduce my childhood play-space to my children. I point out trees, grown bigger now, where they can swing, where they can climb alongside the ghosts of those other children that I knew so well, now grown to adults. Now and then I lead them into what were once our private places. Under rhododendron bushes, dark and shaped like tunnels, gloomy caves. Under beech trees tall and graceful, branches meeting like gothic arches of immense cathedrals, then into the safe space beneath a holly tree where no one else dares to go in case the sharp leaves damage them.

I would like to stay forever reliving my childhood, under my mother's wing, but I realise we have stayed too long when one night we hear the anxious voice of my father.

'Sheila, are you awake? Come quick – it's your mother.'

I spring out of bed, run to her room. She is sitting up in bed, clutching her chest.

'I can't breathe, can't get my breath.'

'Phone the doctor Dad.' He runs to do so. I try to calm my mother. I get her a drink of water. She is shaking, crying a little. She is obviously frightened. So am I. I can't bear to think of life without her.

The doctor has been.

'She's fine. Her heart is strong. She had a panic attack, I believe. Is she worried about anything, stressed do you think? Trying to do too much?'

I look around. My mother's house has been commandeered by a young family. She shops for them, cooks for them, entertains them. Yes, I help of course, but she largely takes responsibility.

'It's our fault,' I say, 'and it has to stop. We have to leave, have to find somewhere to live.' I feel as though I am killing my own mother. I refuse to allow her to do anything for the next few weeks except sit in her rocking chair, read or watch TV. Of course, she insists on knitting jumpers for the children and rocking the baby when he won't settle. But now I am restless. I am panicking . We must find somewhere to live. My schoolteacher husband has found a job, selling educational books to schools. He has no faith in the books, doesn't believe they are all they should be. He hates the job but we need the money. We go to look at houses in Kent, cheap houses, small and full of second-rate D.I.Y. work. My brother comes to our rescue.

'Come up here and work for me,' he tells his brother-in-law. 'You're an engineer aren't you?'

'Well, yes. I'm qualified to teach metal work and wood work.'

'Just the job. Get yourselves up here.'

We go to Newcastle-upon-Tyne, taking the baby and leaving Mum, now recovered, and a friend of hers, with the other three, in a caravan for a week.

I am pleasantly surprised at what we find. Newcastle is a big city. It is cleaner than I expected and not every man wears a cloth cap. We go to view the coastline. Wild seas and miles of sand-dunes. Out of the mist, castles appear defending Northumbria from a history of invaders. Then inland to glimpse the staggeringly beautiful Cheviots. We enter valleys with waterfalls thundering over cliffs into the rivers, which splash and tumble towards the sea.

'The children will love this place,' says their father.

'Think of the picnics, and we could swim in rivers and sea.' I add.

'If it ever stops raining, and you don't freeze to death,' laughs my brother. 'Anyway are you coming?'

We look at each other, then 'Yes,' we say together.

We move in December. I have never felt such cold. There is thick snow hanging over the edges of the roof ready to slide off and envelop any poor soul who is not paying attention.

'Can't switch the electricity on. It's too dangerous. The whole place needs re-wiring,' a professional tells us.

There is no heating in the house.

'We could light a fire,' I say.

'No coal. I'll go and sort it.' Mum is with us, braving the elements. She is back in no time. 'I met a woman two doors down. She gave me a bucket of coal and told me where the depot is.' She hands over the coal and goes to complete her mission.

Sister-in-law Janet lends us an oil stove and thus we begin to thaw out.

The educational book supplier does not give up his job straight away but works out four week's notice. He lives with his mother in Doncaster on week days and is allowed to ply the schools in that area and return to us at weekends. Mum returns to her quiet house to rescue it from the recent invasion. I wonder how we will live without Nana.

So I am here alone in the cold nights with my four young children to take care of. There is still no electricity, which means candles have to be lit as soon as darkness falls and when I hear a cry from a child in the night there is a fumbled search for torch, matches, candles.

Janet takes us in at Christmas, like refugees, like poor relations. I long for a house like hers, with fitted kitchen, central heating and all the warmth and comfort of a family home.

The children start school. James is kept behind in class because he does not know his colours. I am furious I storm into the school.

'So what , if he doesn't know his colours? Ask him them in Arabic and he'll tell you. You're the teacher, teach him them in English now, but not after school, when he's only six.'

James has more than one problem.

'I don't want to go back there.' He says.

'Why ever not?' I ask.

'I talk different to them. They keep saying I'm posh.'

'When people call you things like posh or a snob or a swat it's because they're jealous, James. It means you are different, yes, but it means you are an individual and that's good.'

James looks unconvinced.

'He can't understand all that Mum. It means your special James,' says sometimes very wise Michael.

It is just a year and a few months since we arrived here, to begin a life that I meant to be so perfect for us all. But I cannot hold together something that is so close to disintegration. I know that my husband is having an affair. I have found the photograph, marked the quick and furtive glances, noted the touching, the tear that was not brushed away quickly enough. I feel the desperation of someone who knows she cannot stop something that is out of control, the helplessness, and finally the resignation.

The resignation, mixed with resistance in believing that my husband and my best friend could do this to me, and worse, that they could do this to our children.

I am rehearsing a mystery play with the local church and break down as I say the words, 'Take example all you that hear and see, how those I love best do desert me.'

Such blackness, impenetrable, so that I cannot see her face, but I know it is there. My anger is so fiery it should light up every hollow of this Scottish camp-site but still I am unable to see if those cheeks, those so smooth cheeks, are blushing with shame, embarrassment or even pleasure.

'I told him that if you asked me, I would have to tell you,' her voice from the dark.

'And you are eager to confess,' I think. But my anger is not just because they are about to upset so many lives but that they would not admit the truth until now. All those weeks when I have known that there is something, the times I question him and he denies it. I hear my voice, as many others no doubt do, ring out across the camp site.

'Don't you ever touch my children.' I don't know why I say it or even really what I mean, but I am their mother and my baby is only two years old. I know our lives must change, time and again, not just tonight – but he is only two.

I find myself upon the beach, sitting on the cold sand, hugging my knees, rocking in my sickness. I can hear the sea, so calm, like me somehow both of us rocking quietly, intensely. Now and then a sob as the next wave turns over.

I don't know how long I have been sitting here, it doesn't matter. When I get up I have to begin again, a new life, and I have to be strong. There is no one else who can do what I know I am going to have to do. Someone walks along the beach. I stay quite still. I don't want to have to speak, yet I long for someone to comfort me and understand my fears. He passes by and I am left to rock in my self-pity.

Such a terrible and beautiful night. Stars have brightened the blackness and the moon begins to rise, dripping bright drops into the sea. The sand I sit upon is solid, held together in its dampness, it feels secure somehow on this night, but tomorrow when the sun comes up, warming and drying, it will explode into so many tiny pieces, and what of me and my children, what will daylight bring to us? The breeze blows on my wet face. I am crying for all the lost things in my life. The little gold chain and pendant that I loved, lost on a foreign beach somewhere – the leather shoulder bag, that though I was a child made me feel a woman, lost in a cinema long ago – the twins that were born so still, and now, a marriage that was to be happy ever after – lost, all gone.

Yet not everything is lost. I stop my rocking. I hold myself in an embrace. I can manage. Life may change but I am strong enough to carry on. Women do, Nana taught me that. 'Don't expect to get over things, you have to go through the middle, there's no way round. All you can do is learn to cope.'

But I want to do more than just cope. I want to be happy and even more I want my family to be happy. I walk to the sea. The moon has made a pathway across the water. I dip my hands in and bring the coolness to my burning face. I am shaking. I am not strong at all. I am weak and scared, and worse, two people I trusted once completely have rejected me.

But that is how it is. Those are the facts. I am stuck in quick-sand. I drag each foot out one by one, the suction making a noise, like water down a drain. The holiday, if it was a holiday, is over. I walk back to the camp, to my sleeping children. I see two shapes close together like shadows. The moonlight catches on smooth skin and for a moment lights up another face so familiar that at times it has become my own. A cloud shuts out the moon.

I lie awake listening to the sounds of children breathing, asleep, oblivious of the chaos that is soon to crash around them. Is it possible to turn your back on what is part of you, your flesh, your blood? For me, never. I sleep. A sleep of great release, truth at last admitted.

This morning I am first to wake and walk out into the beauty of a world I have not seen during this week.

Mountains are clear cut, colours are vivid. I wonder if I am still asleep, whether I should walk into the ice-cold sea so crystal clear and shock myself awake. But the ache inside, the feeling something is very wrong, the feeling I woke with and I know will stay with me for a long time, convinces me this is reality.

I go to wake my children.

After the holiday he is soon gone. I take stock at what I am left with. I tour my house. At least we have one fitted carpet in the front room, even if it is a cheap one. We also have a gas fire, which means we have one warm room. There is no heating in the rest of the house. There is a large hole where the fireplace used to be in the breakfast room. But the wiring is done, for which I am very thankful. There is a leak in the bathroom ceiling which shows every time it rains. The wall in the boys' bedroom is crumbling away. Cavity walls are a nightmare, I decide. One room has been partially decorated. Every other room needs doing.

I start with the front door.

'Why are you painting it that colour?' Jacquie asks.

'Lemon yellow is fresh and bright and different, besides I got it free with the bargain cans of white paint I bought, and I like it.'

Everything else in the house gets painted white. It looks bright and clean and has a hint of Greece and other sunny places. I even paint the yard white, and grow flowers in a trough out there. On warm days I serve our meals al fresco. The children complain that all this white gives them migraines, especially outside in the sunshine. I search out sun-glasses for them.

I sometimes examine my children minutely for signs of discontent, unhappiness and so on. I notice we still laugh a lot together. I do worry though, being on my own with them. I have always loved a challenge, but this is ridiculous. I mutter this often, mainly when I am faced with the discipline situations. I find it easy to love my children but I am more than a bit useless when it comes to discipline.

Michael has the disadvantage of looking older than his years. Bus drivers question him when he asks for a half fare. Sometimes I expect too much of him.

'You're good at wood-work. You could transform the kitchen.'

He tries, bless him, but he is not yet even a teenager, and the call of his friends, the call of TV is strong. The kitchen is never finished. Along with my painting I am fanatical about polishing every day, making beds, hoovering. I suppose it is because we have so little and what we have is second, or third-hand, that I feel at least it has to shine.

I discover that being on benefits I am entitled to free insulation. The men come in and tramp about in my roof for a day, insulating the loft. Two or three days later I am ironing downstairs when there is an almighty crash and a sound like thunder upstairs. Shouts ring out from the children who are up there playing with some friends. I run, my heart racing, taking the stairs in twos and threes in my haste to see what has happened. I swing open the door of the boys' room. They are sitting unharmed on the beds, their faces as far as I can see registering shock. Almost all of the high and large ceiling has come down on them. Luckily the solid cement pieces of cornice have missed them, but what looks like the dust of plaster and soot has covered them, so that it appears as though their hair has gone suddenly grey. Their faces are masks of black, grey and white. Their clothes and everything else in the room is covered in the same, still settling, cloud of dust. Hysteria takes hold and I begin to giggle, soon completely out of control. The children join in and it is some time before we can think about how we can put them and the room to rights.

I call the insulation people and tell them it is all their fault, tramping about in the roof has caused the ceiling to come down. I persuade them that that is why they are insured, in case they cause problems like this. For some reason I will never understand, they agree to plaster the ceiling. I ask them to 'just do the wall as well'. They do.

That night there is a storm. I claim from insurance for the roof over the bathroom. I say it must have been damaged in the storm. Well it could have been made worse anyway. They fix it. It's true what they say up here in the North East. 'Shy bairns get nowt.' I shall have to be brazen more often. Things are looking up, things are getting done.

I continue to have restless nights, dreaming of crumbling cavity walls.

## Michael's story

I'm the oldest son. Dad said I have to be the man about the place. I start at Comprehensive School today. I find it a bit hard being told I must be the man about the place. I want to put scruffy jeans on and go off and play with my mates, but now I feel guilty doing that, so sometimes I hang about at home doing nothing. I annoy my sister by lying across the fire, tapping my foot on a rattley bit and watching T.V. I feel bad about that too. I know Mum doesn't expect me to be a man yet. She thinks she's the man. She paints the house, top to bottom, mostly white, because she got a 'bargain lot'. She sways about, high on a ladder, with a paint brush strapped to a broom-handle, so she can reach up to the highest places, even the top-most sky-light.

I feel a bit worried, afraid for us, me and my sister and my two young brothers.

'Mum, don't fall. Who will we have if anything happens to you? Who would look after us?'

I see her stop and wonder.

'Oh, nothing's going to happen to me,' but she looks around her. 'Hold the ladder steady, will you Mick?'

One day I wait until the others go to bed and just she and I are on our own.

'Mum, you'll be getting a letter from school.'

'What about?'

'I got strapped,' I begin.

She is horrified, 'Where, where? Let me look.'

'Mu-um' I say, but she has taken my half offered hand and kisses it.

'How dare they.' She is angry.

'Mum, I think you're supposed to ask why, not where.'

Then we start to laugh and laugh at her reaction.

'Smoking isn't good for you,' she tells me later.

'I know, and I didn't like it anyway.'

She catches me one day putting plastic bags into my shoes, because they leak, and I want to go walking in the hills, with the Scouts. I don't mind. It's quite fun for me, but I know she feels guilty because all the money has gone on bills, and she can't afford to buy me new shoes. Later I tell her how I enjoyed the day.

'We walked along, sang songs, and we cooled off in a waterfall and we had a picnic there. We had to go on the train first, and my shoes really weren't a problem.'

'Well I suppose sometimes we have to do without, or at least make do with what we've got and we still enjoy ourselves,' she says.

I agree with her.

'Like when you make pancakes for breakfast and everyone thinks it must be Christmas or at least Easter, and really it's because there's no cereals or bread and only one egg, and a pint of milk on the doorstep.'

'You're too wise for your years,' she smiles.

'Then we're all late for school, because we're enjoying them so much and you make us all wash our sticky selves again.'

'You're not really late are you?' she worries.

The house smells of new paint and polish and always of fresh baking and once she's sold something to buy a new gas fire, it's warm and welcoming too. There are four of us and we all have friends and she never turns them away. Sunday teas are famous in our street and she makes plenty for all, us and our friends. She bakes bread and other things. She gets out everything that is lurking in the cupboards and says it is her challenge to make things from whatever's there. It doesn't always work exactly as she thinks it will, but it usually all gets eaten.

'That's because you poor little things will eat anything because you're starving,' she jokes.

In the evenings with our hair washed and all smelling of soap and tooth-paste, she reads a bed-time story, little brother on her knee, and me pretending not to listen but hearing every word. I stay on to watch some T.V. programme with her, just the two of us, the others tucked

in bed. Now and then we talk about our plans, what we hope for and try to guess what will happen tomorrow.
Just occasionally she brings a man home saying this one or that one is a friend of hers. We dread that she will try and find us a new dad. We prefer to stay the way we are.

Spring has begun to push its way into the outside world. Daffodils bloom in front gardens. Tulips are beginning to bud and the wild currant shakes its little blossom in defiance of the north east wind. I see this happening from my front window as I glue myself against it, as I do every evening to watch for him coming into the street. I want to stop the seasons from changing, trap time where it is, stay frozen in the moment until he returns. I do not want to live a second without him by my side. He will come back for me. He has no house, no job, no family, but with us he would have what he needs most, he would have hope if we were together, and we could start again. I just have to go on looking, keeping that hope safe for him.

# Part III

'I have more care to stay than will to go.'

The local vicar comes to see me. He is embarrassed, shy, but compassionate. He really seems to care.

'Shall I say a prayer?'

I shrug 'O.K.' I want to say, 'I'll try anything,' but know this would not be right.

Yet the prayer somehow makes me want to talk.

'The police have offered to give me the name and address of a clairvoyant. They said she's helped them before. I feel as though I've begun to clutch at straws.'

'Well, you know what happens when you clutch at straws, you sink,' he replies, 'and I think it's too early to do something like that, even if I believed it would help.'

'You mean you don't believe that?'

He shakes his head, 'Things like that can manipulate, contort your mind.'

'Like ouija boards and witchcraft?' I ask.

'Possibly,' he says, 'but I'm sure there are lots of alternative steps you can take before you start giving up hope in that way.'

He doesn't know, nor do I enlighten him, that I have begun to swing a pendulum. Mine is a crystal, hung on a length of cotton, and in the secret space of my bedroom I ask the questions and wait for the yes/no answers, first establishing the directions of the yes and no.

'Will I find him?' Always I receive a yes. Then through the months of the year.

'Will it be January? Will it be February?'

'Should I look here — should I look there?'

There are always answers, but are they just what I want to hear, are they coming from my subconscious? I look back at the vicar, 'I am so desperate, you must understand. I am afraid to leave the house, afraid that he will come while I'm away. I'm afraid that I might miss a phone call telling me he is safe. I am frightened to see people, to talk to them because it turns this nightmare into reality.'

He is sympathetic, but I know his kindness cannot really help me, so I stop talking again and soon he leaves.

It is a mother's duty to go shopping, something crazy tells me. So I sneak down back lanes, still hiding from the world. I drag myself on leaden limbs, head down believing anyone I meet will know my story and pity me. I don't want pity. I just want to lie down on the pavement among the rubbish and the heaps of what the dogs have left. I want to go to sleep there and let the rain dissolve me and wash me into the gutter, into the drains, so that I disintegrate amongst the debris of the sewers.

I know the children's eyes are following me each time I move, watching, watching, perhaps waiting for me to make contact with what is real. But I cannot yet break the surface, reach the air.

One night I find myself upon a beach. I have walked there in some confusion, on a night that is warm and without light. I can barely see the silhouettes of fishermen who stand on the shore casting their lines into a dark and oily sea. I think to myself that if I keep walking out deep into the ocean, until it covers my head, and I cannot feel anything but water underneath my feet, perhaps I might drown. Then I might be where Len is, wherever that might be. I listen to the sea and nostalgia for times past flows over me in the sound of the waves, the taste of salt on my lips.

I know Len is still alive. I know we will find him, and too, I know I cannot leave the people I love and cause them pain. And after all, I'm a good swimmer and I know I won't drown, I'll just keep swimming. Hopeless really. I half smile to myself. What am I doing here? Maybe he will knock at the door tonight. I begin to run along the beach, ignoring fishermen who really do not care for anything but bait and catch.

The children's father left, taking our means of income with him. The Social only provides for the bare necessities. I need to make some money. My children suffer and walk round in shoes that let in water. Michael wears plastic bags inside his, so that he can go off hiking with his friends. I feel ashamed and guilty, and angry too that all this has landed on my head. I feel I cannot cope sometimes, and yet I have to. I don't want my children to miss out, and sometimes they do, for lack of funds.

I wake in the night tossing and turning, unable to sleep, near to panic at the huge responsibility that is now all mine. I need money and am qualified in nothing except hairdressing, and my qualification is probably worthless now. There are modern ways to colour and to perm and I do not know these ways.

Friend Ella and I talk well into the night, drinking too much wine, immersed in misery or bursting with new ideas, or hysterical with laughter at our money making plans. We do embark on designing soft toys, but often cannot see for tears of mirth or despair which alternate in all we do. Our

Scottie dog looks more like the Loch Ness monster and we finally admit defeat in this department.

Then one day Ella comes to see me. 'I've got a job,' she says.

I try to sound excited at her news. 'Come on then, tell me all about it.'

'Well, it's with a town planning project.'

Of course, she has a degree in something like this. I feel so alone suddenly, as she rushes on with all the details. I have to plan things for myself now. I still have John at home and wouldn't leave him in a crèche. He needs me, or perhaps I need him.

Today Social Services comes to inspect my house. I am to be a registered child-minder. They O.K. me, and say they will be in touch and send me my first 'client'.

A little Indian boy arrives, with his mother. She brings him every day for two weeks or so, then, 'I shall not be bringing him again. It is better for me not to work because I lose my benefits.' Anyway, I think, he's only little, he needs his mother around.

A string of children arrive one after the other. The mothers, usually on benefits, discover they cannot live on their wage as their benefits are removed. They don't work for long. One woman comes to pick her child up from me, for the last time.

'They caught me. I was 'fiddling the system' they say. They're going to take all my earnings back out of my benefit money'.

I look at her little boy, strapped in the push-chair now. It is a cold day. He has no gloves or hat.

'Wait a minute,' I say. I go and fetch some of John's.

'No, I can't take them,' she says.

'Of course you can,' I say, and put them on the little cold figure. I can buy some more when I get Tuesday's family allowance. Until then I'll put John under a blanket.

Registered child-minding ends when I acquire Rosie. She is a strange bulky child. She never says very much, just grunts a lot. I feel a sort of love for most of the little ones in my care but this one I can't somehow bond with at all.

It's cold weather. Is it always cold weather? The gas fire is on and under my supervision the young ones play, more side-by-side than with each other. I suddenly remember the bin men are about to come down the back lane and I haven't put the bins out. I see that the children are settled and I hurriedly put all the rubbish outside the back gate, then I close it and go back to the house. The back door is firmly closed and with a Yale lock. I do not have a key. I am unable to get back in. My heart plummets. I rush to the back breakfast room window. It too is firmly closed. I look through. Rosie is in front of the fire and with difficulty, is peeling off her garments one by one, slowly and carefully. I run out of the back gate, down the lane, behind the terraced houses and round into the front street, to my own front door. I pray as I try to push it open. It doesn't yield at all. I call to John through the letter-box.

'John darling, come and let mummy in.' Joy! He understands and comes running to the door.

'Open the door, darling. Good boy.'

He can't reach of course. I am almost in tears now. I run all the way round the house again, and panting and crying, I look through the window. Rosie is naked now, except for her socks. Her clothes are in a heap too near the fire. She sits down and begins to pull her socks off.

I'll have to smash a window. Then I remember, Michael and his friends got in when I was a little late getting home one day. There was a faulty lock on the front room window. I run again down the back lane and along to the front of our house.

'Let it be alright, let it be alright.'

My heart is pumping. I strain and push at the window. It's an old sash type and heavy, but I can't shift it.

'Help me,' I moan. Then it begins to move and I push with all my strength. When there is just room for me to squeeze through, I lean over the ledge, wriggle, and fall in a heap below the window, but inside. 'Thank you God' I say. I can smell scorching. I race into the breakfast room. Rosie is holding her shirt too near to the fire. 'Get warm,' she says. I have only ever heard grunts from her before. I snatch the shirt from her and pull her away from the fire. I start to laugh, with relief. John joins in, although he is too little to understand why we are laughing. Rosie doesn't laugh.

When her mother comes, I say, 'I'm sorry, I'm giving up child-minding.' She is disappointed. 'Make sure you get a really responsible person to leave Rosie with, won't you.' I say.

'I thought I had,' she replies.

It is Ella who tells me about the British Council.

'You have lodgers for one week to a month. You just give them bed and breakfast. All they need is a room of their own to sleep in, with a desk to work at. They are all mature, overseas students and will stay with you when they first arrive in this country, until they find a permanent place to live. British Council pays well.'

'What about my benefits.' I have seen what happens to so many of the women whose children I have cared for.

'No. It's O.K. The money they pay is so you can look after the lodgers. It pays for breakfast, electricity and so on.'

A stranger in my house. Do I really want that?

'They're vetted by British Council,' Ella continues reassuringly.

'So I'm guaranteed not to be murdered in my bed,' I say.

'You're a big strong girl,' she laughs.

'You realise I would have to sleep downstairs on the settee.' I say

'As I said, you're a big strong girl.'

That's two weeks ago now. Things happen quickly once you give the word. Another inspection of my house and although the word 'shabby' comes to mind, it is clean and warm, so is given the O.K. once again.

Expecting my first guest I feel more than a little apprehensive. The children are quite excited.

'He's from Gambia,' I say.

'Africa, Mum?' says James.

'Yes.' We look at the map together. Even so I don't think we are as prepared as we believe we are, when I open the door. I manage to shake his hand, invite him in, trying to appear unperturbed. The family however are struck dumb. The height of this man is immense, and his skin is blacker than black. His face looks as though it has been carved in wood, chiselled out features, full and strong. To add to this he has tribal scars on each side of his face. Spectacular! I think to myself.

I try to bring the children back to life. They are staring open-mouthed.

This evening he gives me presents crafted in his own country by his own people. A wooden mask which speaks to me of Voodoo and witch craft.

'Thank you,' I murmur. Do I really want this hanging on my wall?

An ebony paper-knife, more like a dagger really, with a carved female on the end. I know she is female for she has small pointed breasts. Her head, too large for her body is smooth, no pretence of hair. She has slanted eyes that look swollen, puffy. Her lips are like his, full and pouting, under a wide-spread nose with cavern-like nostrils.

They too are like his. I am staring now at these nostrils. He looks up catching my eye.

'Thank you.' I say again. I tear my eyes away from his, but things get worse.

He is squatting quite comfortably beside my chair. He is so 'native' somehow, and I have a sudden vision of him in loin-cloth and a string of beads. The air is filled with the sound of drums. The door is flung open and Jacquie storms in,

'Mum, tell him to turn his music down,' she shouts, 'I can't hear myself read.'

I drag myself back to reality. Michael's music is pulsating through the house. I go to sort it out.

He has been here almost two weeks. It has been strange having him around my house, not because of who he is, but because he is not a member of the family and we are not relaxed, always conscious that he is around, on our best behaviour, as it were. Tomorrow he will be gone and our first taste of bed and breakfast hospitality, of me being a landlady, will be over – next time must be easier.

Tonight he stays up a little longer than usual. The children are all in bed. He comes to where I sit, squats in his easy way beside me. I smile at him, knowing he will be gone tomorrow, wanting him, I suppose, to take away a good impression of his first English landlady.

'Are you looking forward to being in your own place?' I ask.

He doesn't answer but his long arm snakes out towards me and his long fingers press themselves onto the back of my head.

'I think you would like to know what it is like to kiss a black man,' he says.

The scars on his face are close to me now and I can see clearly that one of them is longer than the rest as though the knife has slipped. His full and yes, voluptuous lips are inches away from mine.

'Actually, I know what it is like,' I say, offering no more explanation. I stand up, leaving him, for once, looking small below me. I turn off the music.

'Turn the light out, when you go to bed please,' I say. Then I go and lock myself in the bathroom and wait until I hear him pass to his bedroom.

I go back downstairs then, for having bed and breakfast clients means I must sleep on the settee, though I try not to let my lodgers know this.


In between our guests we become a little wild, eating our meals by the fire, in front of the television, sometimes in our dressing gowns. We walk about with no shoes on, leave the washing up until the next day, play our music too loud and invite all our friends in. We have a series of interesting characters to stay. There is a Sri Lankan woman doctor, who believes she knows better than me. Knows everything better than me.

'You mustn't let your children eat those.'

'You shouldn't let your children do that.'

'We must go to bed now, it's late,' this as she turns off the television and the lights. But I am patient. I can take it. I am being paid and she will be gone soon

The five foot two Hungarian, a true romantic, stays longer than the others. He cooks goulash for us, teaches us the Czardas, buys gypsy LP music for us and pours Bulls Blood for me. He discovers I am sleeping on the settee and offers me the chance to share his bed. When I refuse, he curls up on the threshold of the sitting-room.

'I will lie here until you agree to share my bed.'

I close the door and he doesn't stay there long. We take him on a trip to the seaside on the top deck of a bus. He is so excited, like a child going on holiday. He has never been to the seaside, never built sand-castles or felt the strength of the waves as they throw themselves onto the beach. We build the biggest sand-castle we have ever built. We are the only builders on the beach. A few people walk their dogs, muffled up against the cold, and when we have finished, we stand back and admire our work, warm from our efforts. Then one by one we jump on to the castle, crushing it once more into a pile of sand. He stands, mouth open, shocked at our vandalism.

'Well, if we don't do it, someone else will', I say. 'Come on', and with encouraging shouts from us, he finally leaps high in the air, landing between us in the destruction.

We walk beside the sea, tempting it with our closeness, then running to escape the bigger waves. None of us escapes however, and wet to the knees we climb into a steamy bus to go back home.

We actually miss him when he is gone. No two lodgers are the same and in a way, I am sad when all this comes to an end, British Council having found some other way to deal with their temporarily homeless people.

The last lodger is from Sri Lanka, another doctor, this time male and totally different from the woman who stayed with us. He is pleasant, polite, quiet, no bother. When it is time for him to move on, he shakes my hand, thanks me and smiles. I haven't noticed him smile very much. I hardly got to know him really. We chatted at breakfast and a little in the evening, perhaps I should have made more effort. I'm tired though, and I feel the usual relief that I always feel, when it is time to reclaim our house for ourselves once again.

Then just two weeks later I answer a knock at the door. He is standing there. There is a light dusting of snow on him, the white a stark contrast to his dark hair and skin. I often wonder why people choose the north east of England to study, when they come from countries that are hot and sunny. I usher him to the fire and go to make him a coffee. I hadn't really expected to see him again. We sit, talking about his work, his studying, then after a short pause he says, 'I really came to ask you to marry me.'

I think I have misheard, this is so unexpected.

He goes on, 'My father has a tea plantation – you would have servants – a beautiful house to live in. I think you would make a perfect wife for me. I have watched you'–

I interrupt, though I am not sure what I am saying, so unprepared am I.

'In England we marry for love,' I stammer.

'Yes, I love you,' he says.

I pause, try to think. 'I am older than you. I have four children.' I surprise myself by being practical for once. 'I think you would upset your parents very much if you arrived home with all of us.'

'They just want me to be happy,' he says.

I close the door behind him, finally having convinced him that this was all a bad idea.

I go to wash the cups. 'Servants', I think. No, I don't like sharing my house. Warm weather – a tea plantation. Steamy heat, sunshine, and me graceful in a Sari and straw hat, pouring tea on the veranda , while the children play in the swimming pool watched by a nanny.

I pull my boots on – time to get John from nursery.

★

My first sight of Beirut after seven years is an unforgettable moment. The war has done immense damage, and I am sickened by what devastation I can make out, as we fly over the once beautiful city. My emotions, however, are mixed, as beyond the city I can see the mountains, exquisite and mostly untouched by the punishment of war. The excitement I feel cannot be quenched as I move through customs and into an explosion of sunshine, colour, and noise of friends greeting each other outside the airport. There are soldiers and guns everywhere but people seem to be ignoring them.

I have left my children and come to this country, trusting in the information of those who are well informed here, who assure me I will be safe. My fare has been paid, suitcases have been bought, Mother has given me new dresses to wear, pocket-money has been collected for me.

'I can't leave the children,' I say.

'They have actually got a father,' comes the reply.

I have longed to return to Lebanon. Every year since I left I have thought about returning but I have pushed the thought aside. Even if I could have found the money it would have been selfish to spend it on myself. I am tired. I have struggled on the last few years as a single parent. I want to know that there is a chance of some glamour in my life, the sort of excitement that I once knew in my life in Lebanon. I deserve a break. That's what I'm told anyway, by family and friends. I love my children and looking after them is not a chore, it is mostly good fun, even though it is such a challenge. However, three weeks being cosseted by my friends in Lebanon, how can I refuse? I give up trying to justify my indulgence in going on this trip, and submit.

I cannot at first see Emile in the brightness, but after a few minutes I hear a deep chuckle, and an arm comes from behind pulling me close.

'I was expecting a fat grey-haired old lady, and I see this young, beautiful woman.'

'Your eyesight's not too good then.' I say.

His hair is greyer, but we are so very pleased to see each other. We are standing smiling into each other's faces like lunatics. His same old battered VW of seven years ago carries us to his apartment.

'If I buy a new car, someone will steal it. That's how things are at the moment,' he grins, 'but tonight we will forget the world.'

We pass road block after road block, but the soldiers are friendly and wave us by. As we pass some of the 'paying' beaches, I notice they look a little the worse for wear.

'They've become refugee camps,' says Emile. 'Some Palestinian camps have been obliterated, where else can they live?' He shrugs.

This evening, this night, we do in fact forget the world. His restaurant, now named The Ivories, is very different from the Greek bistro with French overtones that it once was. The war has brought prosperity to many of the restaurants and nightclubs that are undamaged. Because of the conflict bored people cannot travel far, cannot spend money on moving around the country, visiting casinos and nightclubs in mountain regions or places further along the coast. The war means they must stay put, and they spend their money on local beaches by day and eating, drinking and dancing by night, in places close at hand.

'I sometimes feel guilty that I have done so well out of such a war,' says Emile.

This little jewel of a place, with a bar shaped and decorated like a key-board is well patronised by a local and wealthy clientele. I have to pinch myself to believe that I am really here.

Emile leaves me now and then to greet his customers, but keeps returning to me offering to pinch me himself, and repeating again and again,

'Incroyable, mich maoul, unbelievable.'

At midnight, a friend of Emile's, Jamil, arrives, and strings exotic, perfumed flowers around my neck. I am overcome by their scent and nostalgia for what went before. We eat homous and tabouleh and all the foods of Lebanon I have tried to recreate in my Newcastle world. Then we go to drink champagne in Jamil's Beefeater, the Summerland disco, the Layalia, a whirl of music, introductions, dancing, drinking, laughing, and listening to the romantic singing of Joe D., French and Italian love songs. Finally at dawn, coming to rest on a Beirut pavement terrace as the sun comes up. Breakfast there at Al Ajami then back to the apartment.

'I've noticed, Emile, you only have one bedroom,' I say.

'Yes, but I have a bath, you'll be quite comfortable in there,' he laughs.

Then he lifts me up and swaying and both of us giggling, with the champagne or just the happiness of being free and together, he carries me into his bedroom.

It is almost mid day, Israeli jets scream across the sky amidst a barrage of anti-aircraft guns. I am, to put it mildly, nervous.

'Don't worry, come outside and watch.'

Others in nearby apartments are outside on their verandas waving Lebanese flags and making rude signs at the Israelis. It reminds me of a sunny day at St. James' Park, with the team winning at home.

'This can happen once or twice a day,' says Emile. 'The guns can't reach them, they are too high up, but they do keep the planes up there.'

He listens to the radio.

'The Israelis have attacked Palestinian camps three or four kilometres from us.'

All this is considerably worrying to me. I want my children to continue to have a mother.

Emile has brought myself and his very jealous Alsatian, Black, out to do some shopping. He leaves us while he goes to do business in a nearby building. I glance back at Black on the back seat. He catches my eye, raises his top lip and growls. I look quickly to the front again. My neck is prickling with the fear that he might attack me. And now out of nowhere jets scream one after the other across the clear blue sky, like huge metal birds of prey, glinting and flashing in the sunshine. Guns, one of which must be in this street, begin to fire at them. Hell has broken loose and to my utter heart-stopping astonishment, Black now jumps from the back seat on to my knee and then down on to my feet, cowering and trembling in a heap on the floor.

I get down with him as far as I am able. When it is suddenly quiet again, I hear the now familiar deep chuckle and realise Emile is beside the car. The dog reasserts himself and snapping and snarling climbs over me into the back seat again, covering his humiliation by trying to look as though nothing had happened.

'No need to be afraid, they're just playing,' says Emile.

'Tell that to your dog.' I say.

Black bares his teeth.

Emile listens to the radio again. 'Some of the planes were Syrian and the Palestinians fired at them, believing them to be Israeli.'

It seems to me there is a great deal of activity from all sides today. I convey my feelings to Emile.

'Yes I hate to tell you this, but there is more happening today than for some time,' says Emile. Later I am dozing on the bed before going out for the evening. I am shocked awake by the terrifying sound of machine gun fire in the street outside. I am so petrified I feel faint. Emile holds me, stroking my hair.

'It's O.K. habibi. They are just cleaning their guns.'

The day after, hearing about panic on the beaches, and then reading reports in the paper, I am somewhat apprehensive about going there today. However, now able to get comfortably into my bikini and with the promise of glorious sunshine on my pale skin, I fall in readily with Emile's plans. We swim in the so warm sea, and lie in the sun, and the men then play backgammon, tric-trac. I listen to the tap-tap of the counters round the board and the good-hearted shouts one to another.

I must look very different from the women around me. They, and the men too, are strewn with gold, round their necks, in their ears, round their arms and even on their ankles.

'Why do they need all this gold?' I ask.

'They have nothing much else to spend their money on. They can't travel or go to Paris for the latest clothes creation,' says Emile.

I can't help feeling the amount of gold on just three people would keep the children and me comfortably for quite a long time. I miss the children already, of course.

The women on the beach seem to have their hair freshly washed and set in the latest styles every day. Unlike me, they do not dive under the waves careless of what they look like when they come up. They have more than one swimsuit and sunglasses to match each one, and most of them wear high-heeled sandals. I wear flip-flops and own a bikini and one other swimsuit. I get a good tan however and tell myself this covers a multitude of faults.

'Black, black, black, a gypsy.' Emile shakes his head at me.

'You'll miss me when I'm gone,' I say lazily.

'For sure, I will sleep seventy-two hours, non-stop,' he says.

We go out to The Ivories every night and then on to dance and socialize our way into the early hours. I make many friends, not the least of these the young barman in Emile's club who chats to me, and keeps me supplied with drinks while Emile gives time to his clients.

I feel drugged in my happiness. Emile and I know our relationship would not survive what is happening in this country, and somehow that makes it even more precious.

'You couldn't bring the children here. It is too unsettled,' he says.

'I know that,' and I do, in my heart.

'I may have to return to my own country,' he says sadly. He is not Lebanese, he is from another part of the middle-east. His mother phones every day to try to persuade him to go home.

I leave him for a few days to go and see friends in the mountain village where I lived for eight years. Emile orders a taxi to take me all the way there. He pays extra money and tells the driver he must look after me.

'You have to cross the green line,' he says. 'Phone me when you get to Brummana.

Don't be afraid,' he says, and holds me tightly. Now I am afraid.

We drive into what looks to me like the centre of the devastation. Crumbled buildings, skeletons of what they used to be, pot holes making the car bump and stall. We are ordered to stop at check point after check point. Young men in cowboy hats with guns over their shoulders order my driver to open the boot of the car. They search it and look through my passport. They are like boys playing at being soldiers, enjoying the power they have created for themselves.

Weeds are already beginning to take hold where once buildings stood, their green shoots creeping their way over rubble like some disease spreading its way through the city. In contrast, now and then there is a certain beauty, where morning glory has reasserted itself and twines amongst the now wild bougainvillea. At one stop we hear gun shots somewhere among the ghost town of ruins.

'They're sniping today,' says my driver.

'Can we go then?' I ask nervously.

As we start to climb the mountain the damage becomes less apparent and I begin to relax. As we approach our village I notice that the trees have grown. There is an abundance of bougainvillea, streaking the hillsides with brilliant colours. People's verandas gleam with pots of geraniums and begonias. The pots themselves are a rainbow of colours. Painted cans and tins of all sizes and descriptions, blue, white, green and on one veranda shocking pink and luminous green, outdoing the bright colours of the summer flowers.

The air is cooler up here, a relief after the hot dust of the devastated area I have passed through. The war has touched this little village in a different way than in Beirut. People do not dare to move far from its comparative safety. They tell me stories of how they survived some of the worst times.

'We lived in the passage for weeks,' says Nadia, the mother of one family. 'Leila cried most of the time. She is a teenager. She was missing out on all the excitement of growing up. Her exams had to be postponed. Her tears were of anger and frustration.'

'Then Nadia had an idea, for us to make a little money, to keep us from starving.' The husband, Farid, nods at his wife.

'I sent him out at night to go to find flour and so on in nearby villages.' Nadia takes up the story. 'Then we baked biscuits and Leila and I went out during the quiet times and sold them in the street. Leila felt useful again and people were glad of a little treat. There was not a lot to be had in the small village shops.'

'The worst part of this for me is being trapped in this village,' says Dana, 'I love to go to Beirut and shop, but that is finished. I am too afraid. I have not left Brummana for months now.'

In spite of the fear, I am welcomed here as though they are my family. Wherever I go, invitations come thick and fast and I am dizzy with the welcome home celebrations. In between the eating and drinking and spontaneous music sessions, drumming and singing and dancing into the night, I wander round the still familiar places that were so dear to me. I look across the valley and up into the mountains, misty in the heat of June and remember how often I was transfixed by the absolute beauty of this same view, seven years ago. I remember sitting out in the cool moonlit night air, comforting a wakeful child and in love with Lebanon.

My last evening in the mountains and Pat with whom I have been staying, gives a party and invites everyone. A truly mountain, Arabic evening. Milhelm plays the drum and sings 'Samra ya samra.' It could be seven years ago. We dance the Arabic way, twirling and twisting like professional belly dancers and laughing at each other's efforts.

'Come back and live here,' says Najwa.

'I wish,' I say.

'We just won't let you go,' says Amal.

'My poor children,' I laugh.

Pat and another brave teacher from the school agree to drive me back to Beirut. It is a hot and quiet drive. The roads are empty most of the way but we have no trouble.

'I hope your return trip is as uneventful,' I say.

They go straight back before dusk falls, but I am even more aware of the danger and uncertainty of the place. I wonder if I will ever visit Brummana again.

Emile and I are together once more and we are determined to enjoy what time we have left. The closeness we feel is deepened by the knowledge that this will come to an end. I will leave and return to my children.


There is a knock at the apartment door. It is six o'clock in the morning. Emile must go down to The Ivories. Hussam, the young barman has been shot dead. He is twenty-two years old. His exams were to take place on July 2nd. He was studying for these during the day and working at night to pay for his studies.

'He was a leader of students. A member of a political party,' says Emile, as though that explained his death.

'Where are the police?' I want to know. 'Why aren't they asking us all questions?'

'The students will sort it out,' says Emile. 'I have to go to the mountains, to tell his mother, his family.'

I am dropped off at the beach. I am upset but have been warned, 'Don't talk about this, only to our close friends. Ask Jamil if his bodyguard can come to work at The Ivories bar tonight.'

'His bodyguard?' I say

'Yes. He was a barman once.'

It is hard for me. I am a fairly emotional woman. I try to speak to Jamil without showing my feelings. He agrees to my request straight away.

'We have to behave as normal. You know this,' he says quietly, perhaps noticing my tear-filled eyes. People are afraid to be involved. No one will admit to anything.

Hussam's body was found on the beach a short way from his lodgings, and his car elsewhere. The horror of war is truly brought home to me. Emile is upset, of course, more so because it happened while I was here.

'I'm glad that I am here and you can share this with me,' I say.

Emile asks us all to keep up a front in The Ivories tonight. 'No one knows what has happened and we must keep it that way.'

The place is packed and pounding with energy. Tonight of all nights everyone wants to dance and talk and laugh, as though they are all trying to obliterate this war by noise and action.

Another sunny, hot day at the beach, sipping ice-cold water and dipping into the sea, listening to the click-click of the tric-trac games and the murmur of voices dulled by the sound of the sea turning gently on to the shore. Peace and warmth, lying half in and half out of the shade of the large umbrellas. Suddenly a deafening noise. I sit bolt upright. Machine gun fire so close, it must be coming from the next beach. People stand up, begin to run. I start to grab my things.

'It's O.K. They're not firing at us,' says Emile. 'There's a submarine out there. Look.' Sure enough just above the water line a grey shape is emerging. 'The people firing are Palestinians. They took over the next beach and live there. They have to live somewhere but they are nervous.'

I photograph the line of people who have run and strung themselves along the jetty to get a better view. I am astonished at their bravado.

My last night here is as I would wish it to be. Emile has bought garlands of flowers to string around my neck. Jamil arrives at the club and we three share dinner together, happily, yet quietly. We go on to say my farewells to others, but we don't venture far.

'There has been trouble all over Beirut today. It's inadvisable to tempt fate,' says Emile.

We all get together at Jamil's club. I dance with each one of the men with whom I have become friends. Jamil buys Emile and me a drink for lovers. It comes in a large bowl supported by naked cherubs. It has blossom floating on it and two straws for Emile and me to drink with. It is made of alcohol and exotic fruit juices. We stare into each other's eyes while we drink. 'Have to make this look good, for our friends watching' I murmur. We try not to laugh, try to look romantic. Afterwards we dance together, in the close embrace of two people who know they will soon be hundreds of miles apart.

'What will we do without you, me and Black?' says Emile mournfully. We go home and drink real champagne together.

I am on the way to the airport but first Emile is driving me around the hotel area. The Phoenicia, St.George and the Holiday Inn. All have been severely damaged during the war.

'Are you trying to convince me that this is a bad place to be?' I ask.

'I feel something in the air today, electric. I expect trouble,' says Emile. 'It is not just the fact that you are going that is making me nervous.'

He reaches out, strokes my head, in his gentle way. 'I am sorry for the trouble, habibi, sorry I had to work as well. Next time I will take time off – the war will be finished.'

I try to reassure him, 'I've had a fantastic time, in spite of the war. Thank you Emile,' I say.

He smiles. 'There is only a very small chance that you might not come back, so we must both look forward to your return.'

We kiss goodbye outside the airport. He is not allowed inside. I am well under control until the plane takes off, leaving ghosts laid but some dreams unfulfilled.

'Behebbik ya Lubnan.'

I turn from my last sight of Beirut, a city damaged and yet still amazingly strong and vibrant.

'I'll just have orange juice,' I say to the steward.

My tears evaporate as I begin to feel the excitement of seeing my children again.

'Keep your eye on the drinks. We don't want them spiked or nicked, can't afford another one.'

'Not many in tonight.'

'Doesn't matter. It's good exercise.'

The music in the singles club hots up and we begin a frenzied dance around the floor. Sometimes not really dancing, but just jumping up and down like kangaroos, panting, and laughing at our own stupidity. Coloured lights flash in time to the rhythm. Fluorescent lights pick out those dressed in white, dazzling our eyes.

'Look, look,' I scream, pointing at Ella's chest. 'Your bra's shining through your clothes.'

She laughs and goes on dancing, shoving her chest out defiantly.

She says something but I am unable to hear. I think for a moment that life can be quite lonely, even at a disco. We are unable to tell who is who because of the strangeness of the alternating dark and light, and unable to hear a familiar voice because of the noise from the sound system. But that is why we're here surely, to bury, cover up, our troubled thoughts of heart-ache and divorce, in a determination to enjoy ourselves, and to hurtle into something like abandonment. Music and pain are all part of the effort to do this.

I wind myself round some startled male and he is quickly eager to respond. Then I feel his loneliness, his desperation. 'Please, no,' I think.

But then he starts. 'My wife left me last year for someone else.'

Well, excuse me while I yawn. He continues, 'I haven't had a woman since then.'

Whatever happened to 'My name's Robert' etc? Anyway you don't need to tell me that, I can feel it sticking like some derringer into my flesh.

I pull away, grimacing at my friend who appears for a moment in a flash of green light. She and I have been singles for five or six years now. We tell ourselves we are not on the look-out for a man. We manage very well without. We have become a bit intolerant of the 'cattle-market' aspect of this place and just come to have fun, not to get caught up in people's 'trying to find themselves or someone special', or wanting to unload their personal problems on us. I signal to Ella and we push our way giggling to our table, glad of cold drinks, cautiously sipping them, making them last.

Then someone is sitting by my side,
'My name is Len,' he says.

'That's a good start,' I say, 'it's usually something like, "My divorce came through three weeks ago" '

'You've been here before then' he says.

For a few minutes we become intensely bound up in something that amazes me with its strength. He leans towards me. I am not really listening to his voice, at least not to the words, perhaps to the tone. Wrapped in his attention I want it to continue but feel the fear. Coming here was not to find somebody new.

I straighten up, catch someone's eye.

'Got to go dance,' I say, cutting in to what he is telling me.

I walk away from him into another's arms. We dance, and I forget. I will not look back although I know he's gazing after me.

'Do you think I'm sexy?' the music plays.

I sing along with others who also will not dare.

Drinking coffee in this noisy city café, listening to the young men chatting to my blonde and blue-eyed daughter, I see Len for the second time.

Is it him? He stands looking down like some bearded captain about to issue orders to those Saturday morning shoppers swirling about below. The beard is something new. Is it a disguise, a way of diverting attention? If so it has failed, for now he has my full and absolute preoccupation. I can see only him. I go like a sleep-walker to where he is. He is pretending that he has not seen me but I know he has. I feel him like some strong magnetic force. His hazel eyes turn towards me, his mouth and mine try not to smile too soon and we are making small talk.

'Is it you?' I ask gesturing towards the beard.

'Could be,' he laughs. We try to keep that little distance that is left between us.

This relationship which hardly can be called such, was just one moment in a singles club, but is ready to burst into life, and now he reaches for my hand and we connect.

T.V. cameras are here. I thought the press had given up on me. Their knocking on the door has almost stopped. I have not spoken to any of them. Others have fended them off, told them I was too distressed to talk to anyone. Now, however, there is a chance of his face being shown to thousands of people.

'If I talk on screen will you show Len's picture?'

'Yes. We will do that for at least thirty seconds.'

That doesn't seem long, but would perhaps be worth it.

'You're not expecting to get shots of me breaking down, sobbing etc., are you? I won't be doing that. I'll say what I have to, then I expect you to stop filming.'

'That sounds fine,' says the man in charge.

The sitting room is crammed with T.V. equipment. Cameras and microphones seem to take up all the space. I manage to answer the interviewer's questions.

'How long has he been missing?'

'How long have you been married?'

'What do *you* think has happened to him?'

'What would you like to say to him if he is watching now?'

I say the expected things, 'Please come home. We love you. We can start again. Material things are nothing without you,' and so on. Then, 'O.K., stop filming now please.'

I feel my bottom lip trembling and the cameras zoom in.

'Please,' I say firmly and they stop.

In the evening we watch the news, and all I am conscious of is Len's face full on the screen for thirty seconds. They have kept their word. And I wonder if somewhere in a room a voice is saying, 'Hey, that's you, isn't it?'

The media like a good story. It sells their papers of course, and attracts more viewers to the T.V. screen. When we find Len's car in that bleak car park, and the police become involved, the story 'hits' the news.

We watch it unfold on the local T.V. programme. We see dogs sniffing their way through snow covered paths, horses between the trees, their hooves slipping now and then on the wintry ground. Police and rescue teams gather for hot drinks and then disperse around the hillsides. It doesn't seem to be anything to do with us. It is all unreal and yet we cannot bear to miss even one edition, one screening. 'It's on again,' they shout and we sip our night-time drinks and watch the same thing over and over again.

John delivering papers early in the morning cannot avoid the headlines each time. 'N.E. business man missing in the hills.' I go to see his teachers to try to stop some of the harassment he has to endure. Children can be cruel.

'Your dad's dead,' they taunt him.

I try to comfort him but how? How do people cope in this situation? What do they tell the young ones? I don't know a single person who is living in this way, just myself. No one I know can really understand, advise, or sympathize, because they do not have this experience.

Then the *Sunday Sun* catches me. For once I answer the door – no one else is in. It is several weeks now since Len went missing. I am surprised by the re-appearance of the newspapers, but, 'We are doing an article on missing persons. We wondered if we could interview you.'

'Will you put Len's picture in your paper?'

'Of course.'

So I agree. They come. They ask questions. They tell me of others in the area, in similar situations. The children of others, teenagers mostly, have run away, gone missing. No one's husband though. What must it be like to have a child missing, to have a child so miserable and unhappy that he or she would run away.

Once, Michael disappeared. When his father left us he walked off into the night. I ran frantically around the nearby streets searching for him. I couldn't go far, because I didn't want to leave the others alone. My relief was enormous when I found him, leaning over the rail looking down on to the traffic on the motorway. I think he was waiting to be found by me. We talked a little, hugged each other and went home.

The *Sunday Sun* manages a centre page spread. They write about our anxious waiting, tell our stories, dramatising where they can, 'and now she waits for that phone call,' beside a picture of me, slightly unkempt, I think, looking sad of course.

There are two sightings as a consequence of this article, but they come to nothing, and no one contacts me to say, 'Yes, I am living in limbo too.'

I do have support of course, in other ways, from friends and family who are my scaffolding when I feel bowed down with it all.

I have a social worker too. He helps me at times, when I am at my most vulnerable.

'We've been offered one or two houses by the local authority.' He comes one day, to drive me round to view them.

'This one has four bedrooms,' he says. 'You need four bedrooms.' I look around.

One medium-sized living room behind a shop, with a minute scullery. Scullery is a good word for it. A lean-to with a sink. Scullery says it all.

Upstairs it's true, four bedrooms. No garden. A bit of a yard open to the street and full of junk. Worst of all, over everything, the all-pervading, overpowering, greasy reek of fish and chips.

'I feel sick,' I moan.

We sit outside in the car.

'We cannot live over a fish and chip shop,' I say firmly. 'You and I stink of fish and chips and we've only been in there for two minutes.' I am angry that it should even have been suggested. 'I refuse to take my children there.'

'I guess that's a no then.' He puts the car in gear and drives away.

The oily smell still lingering, we drive two miles or so further into the city, and eventually pull up. A square, of worn and muddy green, with one or two disheveled trees, does nothing to cheer me. It is surrounded on three sides by council houses and a pub or two and on the fourth by a row of dilapidated shops, three storeys high. Bill leads me to the fourth side. We go to the back of the betting shop and climb the stairs. I follow him round, nodding and grunting. In the front room I go to the window, and look down on to the 'green'.

I cannot fail to see the worn path that leads from pub to betting shop and back. I imagine the unsteady walk and the ache to make dreams come true, by gambling on some useless hack that probably comes in last. Then the trek back across the green, for 'one for the road', and the swaying journey home, to some poor desperate person trying to keep the family together.

'There's enough depressing sights in my life, without that,' I say. 'Besides it's far too tempting for me.' I am only half joking.

He understands and doesn't argue.

Then finally, 'Here are some keys. The house is just across the road on that quite pleasant estate. Nearer to school for John and James.'

'How many bedrooms?'

'Three, but you have said all along, one of you could use the dining-room for a bed-room, if there were two rooms downstairs.'

It's true of course, I had said that.

'Just go and look at it, at least. We have to find somewhere for you.'

That was true too, of course. People were coming to view the house. We were forced into being re-housed. The money from the house would go to the building society, the bank. I would rather it went to the 'little' people we owed money to, but life doesn't work like that. Nana always used to say, 'Much shall have more!' Perhaps she was right.

'We'll go with you, to look at the house.' Mum is staying here with her sister, and Dad and Uncle are with them.

'You go. I'll stay here if that's all right.' Dad backs out. I think it's perhaps because he so much wants to see me happy, and can't bear to face the fact that everything is falling around my ears once again.

It's the best house so far. I know that, as soon as I get my first look at it.

'It's a bit like a country cottage,' mum says chattily. It's built with what I call synthetic material, but it looks like grey stonework.

'The garden's nice,' says Aunt Elsie, and indeed I can see that the front garden is full of spring flowers, almost over now. There will be lupins and delphiniums later on.

Round the door is a wild currant bush with its pungent smell filling the air.

We go round the house quickly. There isn't a lot of it, after all.

'It has character, this house.'

'An open fire. I love open fires.'

'Just needs a lick of paint.'

'Big kitchen, even if there aren't many cupboards.'

Fire my enthusiasm; encourage me to take this step. I know what all their comments are for. They know as well as I do that this time I must say yes. I must leave my new kitchen, my new bathroom, my converted loft, my beautiful house that we have worked on, to make it perfect for the rest of our lives. I must leave all of this and start again here. We move out into the garden. 'Phew! There's some work to do here,' someone says. It's a wilderness, rubble everywhere and roses gone wild with neglect.

'You're tough. You'll soon get that sorted and how nice to have a garden.'

Why do people keep telling me I'm tough when I feel so weak? Is it a kind of brain-washing? If they say it often enough, will that make me strong?

'Alright.' I succumb. I make up my mind. 'But – I won't move us in, until the whole place is decorated and the garden has begun to be sorted.'

I suppose I am tough sometimes.

*Michael continues.*

Our mother has begun to stir, begun to move around the house, this house that we know we must soon leave. She has begun to look for clues. She hunts in every little secret place that she can think of, and we join in this game of hunt and seek.

'I found this phone number written on the edge of the calendar,' I say. And she rushes to the phone with it.

'Is he there? Have you spoken to him?' She phones all the numbers, writes to all the addresses that we find in notebooks and diaries, though we do not know who people are. She tells the story to so many strangers.

'You shouldn't tell them all Mum, he might be back tomorrow. They don't need to know.'

In our hunting we begin to understand the fear that he must have been going through. Between their much-loved books, crammed in on shelves, so tight, we find unopened letters.

'What are they Mum?'

She looks at me, deciding, I suppose, if she should tell me, then, 'They're bills, and all of them red,' she says flatly.

When we hear a knock on the door, our hearts stand still now, and soon we don't want to answer it, for it is never him. The butcher, sympathetic but, 'You've never paid your account since Christmas, the turkey . . . ' Another telling her that the Christmas gift that was so prized by one of us was never paid for and should go back.

The bailiffs arrive to take what they can get. I think Mum would have cut their hands off if they had dared to step across the doorstep. Now and then she finds a streak of energy which flies at anyone who dares to tangle with us, her children. Luckily for the bailiffs they show some compassion when they hear the story and go away.

'I'll go Mum.' I rush to the door so that she doesn't have to answer, though she is often there before me, like a ghost, silent and listening.

'We've come to reclaim the car.' Mum gives them the keys. 'Sorry love, but the payments haven't been coming in.'

'It's all right, I don't drive anyway,' says Mum. I see John's face. He was so proud when Len came home with that car, and took him out for the first time.

'The phone's not working Mum,' my young brother informs her. The shrill ring of the phone is cut off and the ringing has stopped, and we are all relieved, except that she is anxious that now the chance he might ring has gone.

One awful day we find her staring at his photograph with hate, and suddenly she is screaming. 'How could you do this? How could you leave us?'

My young brother starts to cry and I want to smash Len's picture. Like Mum, for a moment I am angry. I want him here to attack with all the violence and rage that is exploding within me. I want him to take responsibility. I want him here to make Mum smile again, to make us all smile again.

We continue our search in a space that is life without him. Like the emptiness in our house when the van has taken everything away. We wander from room to room. I follow behind her a little as though she might fall in her sadness and I will be there to catch her. She clutches at my arm.

'What if one day he comes back and we're gone? Someone new will be here and they won't know him. They might just say. "No one of that name lives here." And he'll be left outside.'

And he will feel like you do now, I think, because someone chose to go missing.

'These carpets still smell new,' she says. She runs her fingers over kitchen tiles, 'And we designed these ourselves.'

My insides are a mixture, thick and heavy because she is heart-broken, yet boiling with anger, and yet again sad and disappointed that it has all come to nothing.

She whispers 'How could you disappear?'

I take her hand and shut the door and we leave. Len is lost, our house is lost and Mum herself is lost.

Later we stand in the tiny place where we have been re-housed. Furniture stands like we do, muddled up and out of place.

'Well, it will be alright when we get sorted,' says Mum.

'It's so small,' says John.

'Yes, but we've got a garden. When the warm weather comes, we can have a barbecue.'

I look out of the window. The weeds must be ten feet high. I tighten my belt. We have to make this place our home, this suffocating little space.

There is a photograph that someone's propped up sideways on the window-sill. I can't see who or what it is, because the sun has wiped the picture out by shining full upon it and dazzling my eyes. I am forced to move.

'May I, as the man of the house, welcome you to Legoland?' I say. 'Oh, come on, let's make a cup of tea.'

# Part IV

'Though it be night yet the moon still shines.'

Sometimes guilt bites at me like an accusing animal because I dare to feel excitement and Len is still lost. The police missing person's bureau brings me sightings.

'Someone who knows him well, saw him in the front seat of a car, which had stopped at traffic lights, in Dunston.'

I persuade someone to drive me there, as though I expect the traffic lights to be still at red, stopping him from going anywhere. I take his photo with me as I always do. I take the picture into every little corner shop where they sell cigarettes and newspapers.

'Have you seen this man? He buys a newspaper every day. He may have bought one from you.'

But lately I already know what the answer will be, and I am tired of chasing to places where I no longer really believe he has been seen. I feel that I must find him on my own, trust my intuition and perhaps my prayers. I follow up each tiny clue that might lead to him.

One day while searching the hills I see a trail of smoke way up on a hillside. I push my way through forest and undergrowth for hours it seems, in case the smoke is from a fire that Len is warming himself at. But I never find the source of smoke. I never find the fire. One weekend I feel that I must be on top of Simonside at dawn and that I might see him on some distant track. Patient relatives accompany me. We sleep up there and trek up to the top at first light. I scan the hills, the paths, the forest clearings with binoculars, but cannot see him brown and bearded, living like a wild man away from the world.

They bring me clothing to identify. It is not his. They bring a tent. It probably belongs to some poor homeless person who tonight will have to sleep out in the cold. It is not Len's. I feel a certain sympathy for the two policewomen. They try so hard. They seem to want so much to find him for me, but I, inside, don't think they will. I know him to be a very clever man. If he wanted to disappear, never to be found again, dead or alive, I know in my heart he could do it.

People ask me often, albeit in a sensitive way, 'What do you think? Is he alive still?' It seems difficult for them to say the word dead, and mostly it is difficult for me to think that he may be dead. There are moments, however, when I believe he would not have wanted to live. Then I answer, 'He would have felt that he had let us down. He knew that we would lose our house, our home, as well as everything else. He would have felt desperate.'

Still, this does not stop me searching. In town I look at every face I pass. I often forget where I am going in my intense searching.

I have tried so hard to find him, so why now does this guilt bite at me? Why this condemning of myself? Because in spite of everything I begin to feel excitement now and then. I am a student once again. Len had persuaded me, along with my designing of the tiles, to be a part-time student of English and History. He was aware of my love for literature. In my desolation when losing him, I gave up this project along with others, and now my tutors have persuaded me to study full-time.

'I'm not sure that I'm capable of doing that,' I reply to the first suggestion of this.

'Well, we have seen some of your work and we think you are,' is their answer.

Did I mean capable as in intelligent enough, or capable in that it would be really difficult while still searching for Len? Would I be able to give it enough concentration, enough time, when all I really want to do is look for Len?

At first it is hard but it becomes a little easier. I think perhaps I want to complete the course because it was Len's idea for me to do it. I do not want to let him down. I want to fulfill his wish of seeing me in cap and gown accepting my degree. So I find I am able to immerse myself in the romance of Keats, to feel the pain of the woman whose husband was missing, in the poem The Ruined Cottage, part of Wordsworth's The Excursion, and to weep over the deaths of Romeo and Juliet. Struggling with Blake and Eliot I forget, and when I remember, the pain comes flooding back. This time it is not just the pain of Len missing, but the pain of guilt, that for just a little while I could forget.

A day when my lack of hope threatens to submerge me. I am sick and weak from the heaviness of it all. I have to attend a seminar.

'I feel terrible, Jan. Please help if we are asked any questions. Try to answer for me.'

I feel near to collapsing, but manage for a while to sit, listening and yet not listening. Then I lie my head, suddenly, on my desk and close my eyes. Later, I realize it is at that precise moment, my father, the strongest man I have ever known, falls, on a beautiful spring day and dies of a heart attack.

I travel south to be at his funeral, holding myself in, until I see the coffin bearing this gigantic man. I wish that I could kiss him back to life, but it is too late, and I was too far away. I worry about my brave little mother, and it seems she worries about me.

'Will you be all right Mum, on your own,' I ask quietly.

'Yes, of course. I'm not really on my own. There are lots of people nearby who care, but what about you, all the way up there? Don't you ever think of coming south?'

'Well, yes, I do sometimes, but I can't – not yet.' I feel a weak moment coming on.

Mum understands. 'Come on, let's both get a strong drink.' And we do.

Back in the north I stand at a bus stop, waiting to be transported to the poly, back to my course once more. I watch as a baby in her grandad's arms strokes his rough cheek gently. I wonder if my emotions have ever been as raw as they are at this moment. My children have lost their grandad. Two men have gone from their lives, in a way three, though they do sometimes see their father, and I cannot compensate in anyway. I feel feeble and inadequate.

I take the four flights of stairs to Russian Literature. I cannot bear the intimacy of a lift. On the second floor I lean on the railing, thinking I can go no further. My tutor appears on the way to the seminar.

'Are you ill?'

'Yes,' I say.

'Come on, coffee is called for,' and he leads me back downstairs, ignoring my frail protests, trying to remind him that the seminar should begin shortly.

We sit alone in a busy common room and his sympathy draws out my story. It's strange how so few people know what is happening in my life. Yet, not so strange. It's only those close to me here who have heard the tale. I am surprised when first I tell Jan and she cries, surprised and anxious too,

'I didn't mean to make you cry,' I say.

I suppose it is the lot of your nearest and dearest to take the full brunt of any misery. They are the ones you want to talk to. I hate to be miserable. I am naturally a cheerful person who laughs a great deal, but at the moment I feel friends must be afraid to sit near me, for fear of catching the sadness I must exude. I am lucky to have such support that helps me now and then to feel normal, and forget. Once I laugh out loud at some friend's joke and then I have to go away and cry, like some bad child who has laughed at someone's misfortune.

During my weekly tutorial with a male tutor, I feel a strange atmosphere in his small room. I cannot somehow identify it. I feel uncomfortable and don't know why. I cut the tutorial short. I can't concentrate.

'Thanks for your help. Sorry I have to go, but,. . . ' I stammer my makeshift excuses, and open the door to go. With no warning he suddenly pulls me back into the room and slams the door shut. Then he kisses me full on the mouth. I don't respond. He lets go of me. 'I'm sorry Sheila.' He is muttering some explanation. I walk out of the room. I don't shout at him. I don't forgive him. I don't react in anyway.

So, I am still a woman. I still have to contend with all that. God, this is not fair. I feel as though I have committed adultery. I walk purposefully out of the building, through the grounds, ignoring friends shouting my name, expecting to drink coffee with me. I walk and walk. I don't stop until I am locked inside my own bathroom. Then, as though a spell has been broken I spring into life, washing my mouth vigorously with soap, scrubbing my teeth until the toothpaste foams from my mouth making me look as though I am having some kind of fit. I gargle and I spit as hard as I can into the basin. Then I am ready to begin again.

Time is passing and with it birthdays, Valentines. I look for the card I most want to see. It never comes. I fantasize on special days that he will appear and ease my tiredness, soothe my pain. He never does.

Then one by one my children dare to leave. Jacquie goes to live down south.

'Fiona,' (her cousin) 'wants me to go and work down there. I think it might be fun.'

Michael goes to share a flat nearby, with some of his friends.

'I'll be right here when you want me, Mum, and you'll have more room without me.'

James prepares to go to Hull University,

'I'll always come home in the holidays,' he promises.

Now there will be just two of us and we will be as content as we can be. Me immersed in books and writing, and John pleased to have my undivided attention now and then. Time is passing. Len is still lost and I am still searching.

Len and I share picnics in his basement flat when we first fall in love, sitting round his fire on cold evenings. We both love Waldorf salad, and eat cartons of it from the deli. The first time I come to his flat I know already I am very much in love.

The flat is below street level.

'I watch for your legs passing my window, then I rush to open the door.'

'I see. I wondered why I never got the chance to knock.'

After that, because I know he will be looking, I always do a John Cleese funny walk, a goose step or I limp past, then run down the steps embarrassed, as people in the street give me questioning looks. Then he is really slow opening the door, savouring my embarrassment, eventually allowing me to fall in, a laughing heap upon him.

I am pleased by what I see that first time. There are books everywhere, in piles upon the floor and in shelves hanging on plaited ropes. The bed is folded away, a settee for the occasion. I am nervous. I think events are too good to be true, I am glad the bed is folded away. I want to move slowly, apply brakes to what has taken me over so dramatically. Most nights now I lie awake watching the light become brighter and not caring, that I cannot sleep.

We stand in this room, not speaking. There is music playing. It digs into my inside, disturbing emotions that have been cut off too long – but of course it is not the music but the nearness of this man. He pulls me close, kisses me, and brings me the reassurance that I need.

'I want you so much,' he says, but at the same time sets me tenderly away from him. 'But we are not going to rush things.' I know he is aware of my relief. 'Instead we will eat pizzas, drink wine and listen to music. Then I will walk you home. How does that sound?'

I want to say, 'To hell with the pizzas', but the moment is magic even if it is frustrating. The thought of sharing all evening with him is enough to make me feel we have already made love.

Then on a day in October, a fresh clear day of autumn, our wedding day. I wait nervously, with my children, for the mini-bus to arrive, to take me to where we will say our vows and promise each other that we will be together forever.

They arrive, my conservation work companions, friends I have made at my little part-time job. But this time there are no signs of saws and mallets, woodland instruments and the strange objects used to create dry stone walls and clear river beds.

Toilet paper decorates the bus, fashioned into bows and flowers and streaming out like ribbons on a bridal limousine. They have polished up the coach-work until it sparkles and you cannot see the bumps and scratches underneath the glow.

'You look different too,' I say to them.

'Had to make an effort,' comes the answer.

The girls wear dresses, the men wear clean jeans, shirts that for once have seen the iron, even ties. One tie is a boot-lace.

'Improvisation, it's called,' says the wearer, 'couldn't come without a tie.'

'Here, brides always have bouquets.' I am handed a bunch of feverfew. The daisies match exactly those on my new blue dress. I wear a hat and later when I see the photographs I wish I hadn't.

We are too early for the registrar.

'Drive past, go into town,' says one, 'let's show off this splendiferous wedding vehicle.'

People stop and stare and we wave to them.

'I didn't see Len waiting at the Civic Centre,' I say. I am anxious: 'He might have changed his mind.'

'Not a chance,' someone says.

They sing, 'There was I, waiting at the church . . . '

I am too nervous to enjoy the joke. I feel a little sick. Now, whenever I catch the scent of feverfew I feel that anxious moment. I sometimes have to think a while to place it, then it rushes back to me.

'It's O.K. I can see him Mum,' says John. I realise that he has been as anxious as I have. 'Of course he is there,' I say, and he is, pacing the floor in his new suit relieved to see us as we are to see him.

By their presence there, friends and priests bless our ceremony. It is short but infinitely sweet. Afterwards we share a cake and glasses of bubbling wine. Then we two drive away, cans rattling on the road, and confetti caught in our hair.

'I'm as happy as a pig in muck,' Len says.

The day we open up our factory it is raining, a fine mist. I glance out beyond the factory for a moment and through the mist I see cranes, silhouetted along the river bank, looking like huge birds with iron beaks, frozen in a no-man's land, unable to move on. Shipyards are dying in the north-east, and we are on the edge of something that will perhaps resurrect all our lives.

A push on the shutter and it clatters into place above our heads. Before I can step across the threshold in my eagerness,

'Wait,' says Len. He smiles. 'Allow me,' and I am carried, like a young bride, into this concrete expanse, smelling of raw plaster and new paint, barely dry. We stand together feeling a sense of ownership and listening to the clanking of some solitary worker across the river.

'Let's explore,' says Len. We are full of excitement.

I laugh. 'Not much to explore,' I say. Just a toilet, a small office space and one vast room.

But soon it is filled with unfamiliar equipment, kilns and racks and glazes. Pots of different colours in rows, brushes fat as pony-tails and thin as two wisps of hair.

Young people join us and with pursed lips, and tongues between teeth they start to paint. With concentrated strokes, they paint the tiles with glazes that seem dull and pale, but these are just a waiting chrysalis until touched by the heat of the kilns.

When the tiles are baked and start to cool, Len stands with oven gloves, like an apprentice cook waiting to take out a freshly-baked cake. We hold our breath when he lifts the kiln lid, waiting for the end result. Are they cracked, have they exploded? But no, Len has done the reading and the learning and now he teaches us. He removes the still warm tiles stacked one above the other, like silent C.D.s holding in their promise of music. While he finishes tracking from the oven to the table we wait, quiet and still, a backdrop to this melodrama. He places the cooling racks upon the bench. We hold our breath and gather round. Then one by one he slides them out and we see that in the firing they have burst into dazzling colours.

Everyone is talking at once.

'Brilliant, where's mine?'

'Look at this. Fab!'

'Who did this? It's beautiful.'

Colours of rainbows and summer flowers.

Len stands among us filled with pride. Proud of us and proud of himself.

I watch the young people often and wonder at their talent and their concentration. Steady hands and steady gaze interrupted now and then by spontaneous jigging to the incessant music of Radio 2. Now and then artists stiff and angular as skeletons straighten up, stretching limbs that have become rigid while focused on minute details. They sit back, half smiling at what they have created.

'I've got to move,' says one, shaking himself.

'So've I,' moans another.

Then someone jumps up from his stool and starts gyrating to the radio. As though intoxicated by the layer of heavy, solvent smell that hangs upon the air, they all join in, one by one, stretching and leaping about for a few heady minutes, then as the music ends,

'Coffee then,' says one, 'then back to it.' Soon they have resumed their places and begin their work again.

I am not always at the factory. I have a special place at home in the bay window upstairs, where the sun shines in on my new coloured pencils. The warmth brings out a fragrance from the wood from which they are made, so that the room smells like myrrh and pine and forest. I am like a child in my contented happiness in this window. I have been given drawing board and colours, sharp pencils, and equipment to enable me to design patterns and pictures. The young people will take and re-create these and place them on tiles for bathrooms and kitchens. People will lie back in their steamy baths and see beside them on the walls, cobles and clippers. In their kitchens they can glance up from the drudgery of housework and be transported to exotic gardens, foreign seas. They can choose, and we will produce, whatever they desire.

Len is like a child too. He is in such high spirits. I sometimes worry, when he rushes in with flowers for me, bubbling with excitement over a new design or a new plan for the factory. I worry that he wants so much for us.

On the other hand, I usually catch the buoyant feeling. When they all come in at the end of the day, eager to recount and laugh about the day's happenings, over the gargantuan meals I have made, I feel in love with life, and especially in love with Len who has given all this to us.

'Local television wants to film us.' says Len.

'Us? But we have hardly got going yet.' I say

'As far as they're concerned, we're a success already,' says Len. 'We've been given the grants, opened up the factory, orders are coming in slow but sure. Most important of all we have employed six young people, even if two are from our own family.'

They come, setting up cameras, filming Len emptying the kilns, some of us at work painting the tiles. We are a success story on the banks of the Tyne, while shipyards stand still and empty.

There is no one in the house but me. A perfect time to work on my studies. I should write an essay, but can't. My mind is unable to concentrate. I make coffee – look out of the window. The hedge needs cutting, but it's so big and I feel so small. I take the coffee and wander into the garden. I've planted too many trees for this quite small area. When they grow, they will take over, blot out the light, but that will be some years away, they are young as yet.

It's starting to rain. I go back into the little house. I glance at my books spread out on the table. What for? I ask myself. Why am I bothering? Putting myself through the need to meet deadlines, trying to take part in seminars, trying to remember what I read so that I can appear at least a little intelligent. I have no heart for this today.

Why doesn't someone come, ask me questions, give me news? Everything has come to a standstill. I don't know another place to go and search. There are no new addresses to write to, no new phone numbers to ring. No one seems to care anymore. Self-pity takes over for a while and I sob in a weak heap on the floor.

I remember once stirring custard over the cooker, several weeks after the death of my twins. Then, as at this moment, a deluge of grief swept over me and I wept.

'I thought you were getting over it,' my mother said disappointedly.

Putting on a brave face is only helpful to others, not yourself. They become cheerful, confident somehow, as though their care and encouragement have done the trick. Set-backs upset them and so it was then. But how can you 'get over' limbo? I try to get on with life but am actually stuck in this bottomless pit world, and cannot really move in any direction.

This is a bad day. I have to get out, do something physical. I'll go to town, buy myself something new. I walk in, pounding the pavement as though I haven't a moment to spare. I look hard at everyone who passes me. I stare at the buses as they pass, searching him out. In town there are hundreds of people. I look down Northumberland Street and I can see an ocean of faces bobbing up and down, busy, smiling, worried, angry even. I could so easily miss him in this crowd. I feel myself becoming frantic, dizzy with the task I have set myself. How many faces have I looked into so desperately? I find a bench and sit down. I close my eyes for a moment and then with head down stare at the pavement. Let him find me. I've had enough. How many times have I given up, only to start again when something sparks me off, replenishes my hope?

Some days later and I am surrounded by thousands of people. Santana plays music that lifts my spirits. I stand almost in the centre of St.James Park, the football stadium, and I am here because of Len's passion for Bob Dylan. Tonight Bob Dylan will play and I will search the faces of his many fans. I start methodically with the people in the stands, trying to see each individual. I turn slowly, registering the entrance of Bob Dylan on to the stage by the thunderous applause around me, and yet not taking my eyes off the point that I have reached. He sings 'The times they are a'changin' ' and I catch my breath, for I have heard that song so often. I continue through the pain of familiar music that Len loved so much. We should have been here together and if he is alive and in this area I know he would try to be here.

I cannot find him. How could I believe that he would be here? How can I believe that I will find him amongst all these, even if he is here? The children hold on to me as we leave the stadium. I am glad they do that, for whatever reason. In the mass of people I could so easily be trampled under foot. I feel not for the first time crumpled, like a tossed aside screwed up paper bag. I am deflated after the surge of hope that anticipation of this concert has brought me all week.

Sometimes I wake convinced that today he will communicate. I watch the phone as though I expect the hand-piece to jump up and hold itself out to me. I look out of the windows back and front continually, knowing he will be there, but perhaps nervous about knocking, in case he is turned away.

I am so full of hope today, perhaps it is because the sun is shining, or perhaps my intuition is at work again. The knock at the door sends me rushing to open it. The two women officers from the Missing Person's Bureau are standing there.

'I thought you were him,' I blurt out.

'Sorry Mrs.Auld. May we come in?'

'Yes, of course.' The feeling of hope refuses to go away.

My upbringing forces me to ask politely. 'Would you like tea or coffee?'

While I am making this I hum to myself, as though I have already been given good news. They sip their coffee and I settle myself, content in my ignorance to wait for what they might say.

Then, 'Have you anything new for us?' they ask.

I am almost shocked. Why are they asking me, I wonder?

'I thought you had come to give *me* news,' I say.

'We have acquired a shirt and some shoes from the region of Simonside.'

They describe them to me. They are not Len's.

'Is that all?' I ask.

'Yes, for now, but we will keep in touch regularly. Don't give up hope. People are nearly always found.'

I don't immediately sink into the quagmire of despair again. The hope that I feel is too strong today. I phone Ian. He is on night shift so should be sleeping, instead he agrees to take me to Simonside. Why I want to go there is unexplainable. Surely it is contrary to the hope I feel, in that if we find him there he will surely not be alive.

Nevertheless we return to those hills once again. It is spring. The larch trees have fluffy new needles on them. The air is so clean, the sun warm. The warmth cannot dispel that damp earthy smell that is always there beneath the pines.

I lag behind, pausing for a moment beside a lively stream. It is amazing, the noise of that tiny rill like a thousand voices echoing, bouncing and chattering around the walls of that little valley. I suddenly long for the silence. I recall a film in which a kidnapped person tried remembering the sounds he heard, on his blindfold journey into captivity. The noise that came back to him most forcefully was of a huge flock of geese, honking and hissing and chattering in a cacophony of sound. Nowhere could the geese be located and eventually the noise was discovered to be a river, gurgling and splashing and pounding its way over a rocky river bed.

I close my eyes in the little valley and suddenly I am surrounded by wild fowl, calling madly to each other, fluttering huge wings. In a moment I am lifting off with them into open sky, taking my place in a gigantic V-formation, my neck stretched in an effort to follow. I know where I aim to go – to a place where all my memories are forgotten, my past is blank and I begin from now. Cold water laps over my boot tops. I have wandered, in my fantasizing, into the stream, and into its timeless journey towards the sea. This powerful hillside water can be diverted but not stopped, just like my memories, except that they of course may fade in time.

Ian is waiting for me. We make our way upwards on the forest paths. I stop now and then compelling myself to feel Len, trying to take my bearings from my intuition, willing it to lead me to the exact place. Now and then I walk into the silent tunnels of the forest. The thick trees muffle the sound of birds, the crack of twigs, as some creature scurries into hiding. The ground is thickly carpeted with pine needles, springy and soft underfoot. The air is still around the base of the tree trunks. It is sheltered, closed in, suffocating. I run back out on to the path and breathe clear air once more.

I dread to find him here, yet I cannot stop myself from searching. If I found him, and there was no one else around, I would keep the knowledge as my secret. I would decide how to deal with this in my own way, in Len's way. But what was Len's way?
Ian is close by my side.

'It's beginning to get dark. Shall we make our way down now?'

'Yes'. The numbness enters me again. My limbs are stiff, unyielding. New shoots of bracken are curling up in the early evening air. Another night descends upon the hillside, blotting out the beauty of the place.

☆

What has happened to change Len? How can our happiness ever be marred? What is going on inside his head that I have no way of understanding? I feel a shadow over us, a kind of madness blighting our days now and then. It sometimes manifests itself in his total and overwhelming love for me, his immense generosity.

'Len, this is beautiful, but can we afford it?' I ask, when he presents me with a small but exquisite gold watch.

'Of course we can. Nothing is too good for you. Here, let me put it on.'

Our second Christmas together, and I am embarrassed at the number of presents he has given me. I am worried too, about how much has been spent on the children. The grants we had are almost eaten up and our loan at the bank will not be extended. I am anxious about the amount that has been spent on food. We are a big family but it seems to me we are verging on extravagance, greed almost, and I feel a sense of shame as I try to fit everything into the fridge.

'Did we really need all this?' I venture to say.

'Well, I thought so, but who am I? Take it back if it upsets you.' Len strides out of the room.

I find it difficult to speak up easily. Lately when I make a suggestion or a comment it so often seems to be taken as criticism. I try to be especially caring and wonder if perhaps I do not give him enough time. I am so busy with the children but,

'You don't have to treat me like a baby. I'm grown up you know.'

I long for things to be the way they were. Then suddenly they are again. We walk in the hills panting and laughing and stopping to hug each other.

'This is wonderful. We should have brought the children,' says Len.

'I thought you would like me to yourself for a change.'

'Yes, well that is great of course, but I do love those kids you know.'

As we drive home it is evening, stars begin to appear in the sky one by one until it seems there are no spaces left for even one more. We stop the car, and huddle together in the cool night air. Len points out different stars to me, but I find it hard to look at them for I just want to look at him, at his dear face that I already know so well and love so much.

Life is like a switch-back, up one day, down the next. I wait each morning to discover what will be the mood today. One day I lie awake. Len is downstairs. I hear him making coffee. On good mornings he and James, like two old men, sit putting the world to rights, sipping their coffee, and enjoying the early part of the day together. He comes into the bedroom puts the coffee down. If only he would speak but no, he walks towards the door.

'Len,' I say, but he does not answer.

I think to myself in despair 'This is not normal.'

Now there are times he will not communicate at all, but sits alone in another room, his outdoor coat on, even with the hood up sometimes. I do not understand.

'Tell me what is wrong Len. I want to help. Is it the factory? Please talk to me.'

'It's nothing.'

'Shall I get you some coffee, something to eat?'

'No. I'll get it, when I want it.'

I telephone Len's sister in desperation. I'm glad I did. It is a sort of reconciliation for them. She is much younger. They have spent many years away from each other in the past. Yet it is she who persuades him to go to the doctor, goes with him in fact. 'Clinical depression,' is the verdict. He is given pills. I am given nothing, no advice on how to help, no information on this illness. I am lost in the incomprehension that I feel. I do not know the questions I should ask.

Today he comes home at midday, shouting my name as he comes through the door. I run to greet him and he hugs me tight.

'Let's spoil ourselves. Lunch by the fire.'

We sip hot soup for lunch, warming ourselves inside and out. We watch the T.V. news. A Russian minister has died. We are an island, Len and I, complete and isolated from all the turbulence of life outside this little room. These moments are a still upon life's movie screen, before the celluloid begins to tear, then splits and flies apart and lies tangled in a heap, later to be swept away. The February fog is thick outside but we are sunshine here together.

He is calm, quiet, and I respect his silence. Now and then our fingers touch and linger as we pass each other bread or salt. 'He is my life,' I think to myself. All the horrors that may come to me in this life will be nothing, because he will be by my side, to care for me, as long as I live.

'I know you are worried Len,' I say quietly. He has a meeting after lunch when business giants could crush us underfoot.

'We could lose both house and factory,' he says.

'We can start again,' I say. But he does not want to hear that. He wants so much for us. Before he leaves he holds me close to him, silently. 'I love you,' I say.

'I know,' he replies. The passionate way he crushes me to him tells me only of his love, not of his desperation. Then, he goes.

☆

*Matty's story*

On Monday evenings we dance rock 'n' roll. The guitar plays and we twist and move in the lamp-light, our shadows keeping time on the high walls of the railway bridge.

'Where's Bobby tonight, Matty?' she asks.

'He'll be here. He wouldn't miss his soup and the chance of a hug,' I reply. 'Any news for you?'

'No,' she says, 'but thanks for asking, Matty.'

Monday nights are the highlight of the week for many of us so-called down and outs. We filter in from all about town. They listen to us here, when we talk about our problems. She always listens to me, and I tell her one night, 'I'm going to stop drinking and if I stop for six months in a row, I'd like to take you out. I'll clean myself up, trim my beard, and cover up my tattoos. We'll have more than lamps and soup – wine for you and candles on the table and I'll drink only tonic water.'

'O.K. Matty. It's a deal,' and I know she means it.

Still she finds me, lying passed out among the shoppers at the foot of Grey's Monument, surrounded by other swaying, sprawling drunks. I become aware of her for a moment through my cider haze. I grope around for a half-empty bottle.

'Have a drink,' I say, waving the bottle in her face. Then I begin to cry. I am ashamed perhaps, or just frustrated that I have yet again blown it.

When I meet her for the first time at the soup run, the braziers are crackling away and the storm lamps shine bright beneath this high arch. Occasionally a train rumbles overhead.

It is an evening of many 'mornings after'. She chats to me, links my arm and I feel warmer than the fire could ever make me. Each week we share in the food, the coffee and the singing. She never eats but sips coffee in paper cups and sings and chats, making her way round, trying not to miss anyone.

'Why do you do this?' I ask, one particularly cold evening when snow is blowing through the bridge.

'I have a reason Matty,' and she tells me, our eyes smarting in the smoke from the brazier.

Turns out she isn't here for us alone, us homeless, drinkers, druggies.

'My husband Len is missing and I think if his mind has gone, if he has forgotten all the best things in his life, he may come here for soup and comfort.'

I notice that she searches all our faces, even mine, though my hair and beard are red. She tries to see under the hoods of tattered coats, beneath the stubble, through the often matted hair and scruffy beards, hoping to find him here. She is here every week waiting to check everyone, looking long and hard at faces that often do not want to be seen. She is always searching, even when she's listening, or comforting us. Then we join hands and sing, 'We shall overcome.' She smiles at me. Then we sing, 'Let there be peace,' and people drift away, find a dry place to sleep. She hugs a few of us and says, 'See you next week.'

✮

I wake suddenly in the night, alert and listening. I'm alone in the house, John away with a friend. My heart is pumping away in the silence. The dog would be barking if it was a stranger but he is silent too. I was probably dreaming. But – it was Valentine's day yesterday, two years almost to the day that Len disappeared. I try to suffocate the hope that I feel rising. I still love him, search for him, miss him desperately.

I waited for the postman yesterday, but as always I was disappointed. I know I will be buoyed up with hopes again next month when it is my birthday. I listen to the thick silence. A car pulls away in the street. I imagine to myself that he had come to leave a Valentine present. He is not ready to come back yet but wants me to know he loves me. I get out of bed and go downstairs swiftly. The dog is in the hall, usually at night he is in the kitchen. I try to push the living room door open. It seems to be barricaded the other side with the settee. I push hard until I can squeeze myself through. The window is wide open. I am nervous again now. I call the dog through. He hadn't barked therefore it must have been someone we know.

There is a space where the video used to be. The television has gone also. The table looks bare and I remember John left his Valentine gift there. His girl-friend had given him a gift-wrapped bottle of champagne and teddy-bear. I look around. There is no beautifully wrapped present for me either, glistening with sparkly paper, hearts and ribbons. Perhaps that has been stolen too.

I ring the police.

# Part V

*'Night's candles are burnt out,
and jocund day stands tiptoe on the misty
mountain tops.'*

I trail the lipstick round my mouth and force my lips into a smile. A grey hair salutes me in the mirror. I smooth it down. Should I pull it out? No. If I keep doing that I'll eventually be bald. I succeed in tucking it in, only to see another standing out at right angles above my ear. I search my face. I swear that's a new laughter line grimacing beneath my right eye. I do allow myself to laugh now and then. I don't want to lose my friends and they like to laugh. The children too like to laugh, and I hate it when they cut their laughter short for fear of hurting me. I look once more into the mirror. Ready now.

But suddenly I'm caught up with a terrifying thought. If Len and I grow old before we meet again, we may not know each other, recognize each other. If our hair turns grey, of if he grows a beard again and it is white, how will I know it is he?

'Are you ready?' My escort is anxious to get to the cider, listen to the folk music. He calls from downstairs, and I compose myself, prepare myself, and after all it is not so difficult. He is kind to me. He expects nothing from me more than my friendship. I feel protected, safe in his company. He wards off attention that I can do without. I enjoy the folk scene too. Len used to take me to the folk clubs, so they are not new to me. They do not challenge or threaten me.

Halfway down the stairs, I stand dead still, almost before I hear the tap at the door. My friend opens it, then he calls my name. His voice sounds strange. Suddenly I know the nightmare has had a kick-start, must jolt me out of my complacency, my automatic searching, my limbo existence.

Two policemen, I recognize one of them, are standing at the door. Through the door I smell the odour of chrysanthemums, and think of Lawrence and my literature course, due to finish next year.

'May we come in, Mrs Auld?'

'Yes, in there.' I indicate the sitting-room. I close the door.

'Is it all right?' He gestures towards my companion,

'Yes. He's a good friend,' I say.

'You'd better sit down,' says the policeman with the familiar face. I feel sorry for him. He is finding this hard. Now my intuition is on full alert. I see the snow, the forest, and the horror of that so beautiful mountainside.

'A party from Scotland was visiting the hills, orienteering. Two of them went off the path.'

'It is him, isn't it?' I say. They are trying to smash my hopes upon that hillside.

'There was a credit card,' says one, 'with his name.'

'It could have been stolen,' I say.

They do not answer, at least I cannot hear. The blood is rushing, pounding in my ears.

'Wait a moment.' My breath is shallow. I have to let it reach my lungs but it is so difficult, when my heart is thumping so hard that I think it will explode. Everything is muddled up. I feel as though I have lost all co-ordination. If I can just get my heart and lungs sorted, maybe then I can work on my limbs that are set in concrete and may never move again.

'Drink this.' I gulp the water down as though I want to drown in it.

'I'm all right now – go on.'

'We'd like you to come with us to look at some clothes and a few other things.'

'They're his, aren't they?' I say loudly. 'You know don't you?'

Why don't they answer? Someone gets my coat. I am suddenly a mother. 'What about John? He's at Scouts.'

'I'll ask next door to watch out for him.'

'You will come with me, won't you,' I say pathetically to my friend, whose night is suddenly changed from one of cider and music, to one of policemen and whatever lies ahead.

It is dark. There are two police cars in the street. I see a curtain flutter in a neighbour's house. I am put into the back of a car. I huddle in the corner, feeling cold and afraid. My friend sits in the front, and talks to the driver. I am glad he is there and that I am not forced to speak, not even expected to listen. We have to go to Rothbury police station at the foot of the Simonside hills. The journey will take us forty minutes or so. I sit and think, rocketing in my thoughts through all the times we had together, things that were said between us, things that I still want to say. Perhaps it isn't him. Maybe someone he knew died and Len dressed him in his clothes and left him in the forest, and Len is still alive. He is a very clever man. He could do that.

Such a long way through the dark. Yet suddenly we're here, and sitting in a small waiting room with pale grey leather seats. A door opens and a kind policeman walks in.

They are all so kind, so gentle, yet what they have to say is so cruel, however soft their voices are.

'I am going to take you to a small room where all the clothing and objects that were found will be displayed. We just want you to tell us if you think they are Len's or not. Can you do that? Just say when you're ready.'

I say nothing for a moment, then, 'O.K. I'll come now.' I want this over. I want to get back home, renew the search even more vigorously.

They lead me to the small room and open the door. My eyes look all round the little floor where things are laid out. Then I wait until the noise has stopped. A moaning, hurt, animal-like noise echoes in my head and only later do I realize it came from me.

I look slowly from object to object. I slump against the door. Someone catches me and holds me there. I am forced to look at his so familiar belongings. His waterproof parka that made him look so big. 'Macho' we used to say. It has suffered, like me, the weathering of three long years. His fleece jacket. I know so well the feel of it. It has enclosed me in his warmth so many times. I catch a sob in my throat, for I see it has begun to rot. Mildew is growing in white spots, stark on the dark material. His watch, that had ticked away so happily our sixteen months together, has stopped. It is rusty and dull. And what of Len? I do not see him of course. My mind shuts off. I cannot cope, and so I do not, with the thought of Len lying in the forest all that time.

They help me to a room where a policeman sits behind a desk. They give me coffee – it grows cold beside me. This is all real. I am unable to wake up from the terrifying horror of this nightmare.

'I have to ask more questions, so shall we do this straight away, and then it will be finished?'

Finished, after all this time, is this how it must end?

Then I'm allowed to go out into the night, into the cool October air. The dark shapes of the hills crowd around me, pushing themselves into my private space.

But still I see there are stars up there. Hundreds of them. There are always stars.

I walk to the end of the drive and sit. I feel as though I have dropped through space to land heavily upon this wall on which I now sit, all the air crushed out of me. There seems nothing left somehow, just the dank smell of autumn. My life's quest has been taken from me, and yet, I have only seen a few clothes, a few belongings. Am I to believe him dead? I cannot. However it may be, I know I will have to go on searching.

*James' story.*

The journey to Hull could have been the journey to Hell. There haven't been many times that I have been in the company of both my mother and my father, together, since I was about five years old. And here we are in a car, traveling to Hull, the only other passenger being Eleanor, my girl-friend.

On one of my visits to Dad he had volunteered to drive me, and my 'kit' to University.

'Thanks dad,' I say, 'the only thing is, Mum has talked about coming with me.'

'That's O.K. Bring her too,' he says.

When I tell Mum, she hesitates for just one moment, then, 'Well, if it's all right with him, it's all right with me,' she says. 'He does have a big enough car for all your gear, which will solve a problem.'

Now we are on our way. The conversation is a bit polite and stilted to begin with and I have to admit to feeling a little nervous and slightly embarrassed. By the time we stop for coffee though, I realize there is no need for either of these feelings. There is not a trace of bitterness or recrimination in the air. I suppose it all happened a good while ago. It must be twelve or thirteen years now. A lot has happened since. Mum always says 'It's water under the bridge. We have to get on with it.' Dad talks quite sensitively about Len, asking a few questions, being sympathetic.

They talk easily to each other, sometimes even laughing over things that happened in Lebanon, stories about me now and then. Mum has always said that Lebanon was a fun time. They are just like good friends really.

I relax and stop worrying. I am going to live off campus and when we pull up at the designated accommodation, Mum says, 'A stately home no less.'

'Not quite Mum. The beer cans stuck in the hedge do lower the tone a bit.'

'I don't know. They make the place look lived in and friendly,' says Dad.

I am trying to join in with the banter but am nervous for different reasons now. Mum and Eleanor take photos on the steps of the building and in the garden. We go in through the front door and are met by a friendly face and are shown to my room. We are introduced to Pat, a young man who will be sharing the room with me. Mum asks all the appropriate questions.

'Where's the bathroom? Where's the kitchen?' etc. etc.

Pat doesn't know much more than we do. He hasn't been here many minutes either. I know Mum is relieved that I have found a friend, so am I to be honest.

I finally wave Eleanor and the parents off. The women are a bit tearful as I kiss them goodbye. I have a moment's panic as they drive away, a feeling of being very alone. I have never been away from my family for long before. I hope I didn't look too lonely as Mum went off. I know how anxious she gets if we are not happy, and she has enough to think about with Len still missing. I go back in. Pat looks a bit lost too,

We're soon joined by others moving in, however, and things begin to change from the apprehension we all feel, to excitement about our new lives. There's a certain freedom beginning for us. In our leisure time we can just please ourselves now. Second year students pop in to meet us.

One of them says, 'Saturday night is the time to get rat-arsed.'

We like that phrase, repeat it to each other and later go down the pub to give it a whirl. When we get back to our room, Pat gets out some home-made wine and some of us carry on drinking through the night, following the instructions from the second years and getting well and truly 'rat-arsed'.

Pat and I seem as though we have known each other for always. The wine leads us into deep conversation, personal information that probably would have come out a lot later on than now. Pat's family has problems that he tells me about, and I then find it easy to talk about Len missing and the upset that has occurred because of that, and also the sadness I feel about it. Len and I were good friends after all.

'Phone call for you.'

It's Monday. I've been here since Saturday and although we didn't see much of Sunday, we are already well dug-in.

'It's your brother, Michael.'

'Michael,' I laugh. 'I knew he'd be missing me.'

Michael's voice is serious, and at first I can't take in what he is saying. The way he speaks is as though what he is reciting is just a story that even he doesn't believe. Unimaginable somehow. Then Mum's voice, quite strong but breaking now and then,

' . . . but don't come rushing back James. There has to be an inquest, identification. Nothing will be happening for a while and I'll keep ringing to let you know.'

I realise she is referring to the funeral and I try to say the right things, but it is too difficult.

'Love you loads Mum,' I say.

Afterwards I stand for a while by the phone, in the corridor, wanting to feel something, but at first not able to, because of the unreality of this. I suppose it really is him? How can they tell after all this time? I begin to feel choked then. I don't want to break down in front of these new friends. They have congregated in our room to discuss our first day at the Uni. I am grateful that Saturday's wine had made us confess so much to each other. I don't have to explain everything. I take a breath and go in, but I'm afraid my face must give me away.

'What's up, Jim?' The kind voice of Pat.

'It's Len. They've found him.'

'And . . . ?'

'He's been lying up in those hills all this time.'

'Christ!' says someone. 'You need a drink.'

They take care of me. After such a short time of knowing each other, we are already a family, sharing our lives, a close unit.

I receive a note from the University Chaplain, someone from Newcastle had contacted him, told him the story. The note says, 'I called to see you but you were not here. If you need to talk . . .' etc. There were contact numbers, a name. I don't go to see him. I have my own personal pastors in these already true friends.

It's hard for me to stay here and not to rush off home, wanting to help, to comfort perhaps, but mum's right as usual, I shouldn't miss these first important weeks of University. I do worry about her and about John, however, and find it difficult to do nothing.

Mum takes her own advice and tells me that, after a week or so, she will go back to the Poly. It's the last year of her B.A. course.

I am completely 'rat-arsed' again this Monday night.

*John speaks.*

I like to remember the holidays we had with Len. All of us on the boat on the Norfolk Broads. Mum getting up early one morning and coming out of her cabin. She's usually so careful not to wake us but we hear her door slam behind her and a whooping noise from her as she feels herself sliding down a slope.

'There's something wrong,' she shouts. We appear one after the other, rubbing eyes, stretching and yawning. We make our way on deck. Other boats are still quiet in the morning mist.

'You know what we've done,' says Len.

'Tied her up on too short a rope,' says Michael.

'The tide's gone out,' says James.

'Yes, and we're caught up on the edge of the quayside.'

'How embarrassing,' says Jacquie.

'O.K. Let's all get on to the quayside and try to lift her off,' suggests Len.

We do, but she won't budge.

'It's no good, we're going to have to wait until the tide comes back in, to float her off.' Len resigns himself. 'Breakfast, I think.'

I hope people who are beginning to emerge from their sleeping quarters on the other boats won't notice our stupid mistake. I go down below and shall probably stay there so that no one will see me. That's what Mum and Jacquie do every time we start to find a mooring place or cast off. The men start shouting things like, 'Ahoy there' and 'catch the rope astern,' and so on. Mum says men like to use nautical terms, which is all right, until they bump into things or steer on the wrong side of the river. Then she says they should be really quiet and try to go unnoticed. I don't mind really. I love being on this boat with everyone, and with someone like a dad, Len that is, showing me how to fish and how to work the locks.

Mum and Len go off on their own for a bit, leaving us with lots of warnings. Michael's sixteen now. I think he's as strong as Grandpa, or nearly anyway. He and the others make dinner squashed into the small kitchen, or galley is it? There's lots of banter, but still they manage to organize a really good meal. French bread and cheese. Well, there are other things, prawns and avocados, stuff that I'm not keen on, but it does look bright and colourful. Reds and greens, and candles of course. Mum is pleased when she and Len come back.

'That looks spectacular,' she says.

We all sit down and eat. We are allowed wine tonight, though I stick to Coke.

Mum keeps passing her hand over the food in a strange way.

'What shall I have next?' She waves her hand over the olives, picking one up on the way. Then across to the bread.

'Pass the butter,' she says to Jacquie, reaching across quite far enough to get it herself.

Then 'Mum,' shrieks Jacquie, 'what's that?'

We all stop eating and pay attention. Jacquie has grabbed Mum's hand.

'A garnet,' smiles Mum smugly.

Len is positively gleaming. 'We're engaged,' he says.

Michael looks as though he has won strong man of the year competition, and the weights have been lifted from his shoulders. He stands up, lifts his glass and says, 'A toast. Can we call you daddy?'

We all laugh, especially me, for I have realized that Mum and Len will marry and I will in fact have him for a dad.

Eating chocolate croissants on a Spanish beach must be my idea of the best thing you can do in life. Sitting at a table overlooking the sea, I try not to let the warm chocolate drip on to my bare skin. I watch James and Len as they squeeze lemon on to their plate of mussels. The smell of garlic wafts across from their direction. Mum sips her coffee and leans back, her face in the sun. We are all sun-tanned and salty from the sea.

Mum wants to take our photos. She makes us all stand round a statue of a large South-American-like bird. Len makes me climb on top and sit one leg each side of the bird's head. I am sure it will break. So is mum.

'You can get down now,' she says quickly once she has taken a photograph.

'Another one,' she says. 'Turn round now and pull your trunks down just a little so that I can see the contrast of brown and white skin.'

Len hooks one side of his swimsuit under his bum and I try to do the same.

'You always have to go that little bit too far, don't you?' she laughs. She laughs a lot lately.

'I think the best thing you can do in life must be drinking red wine on a Spanish beach, especially when it has been in the boot of the car all morning, in the hot sun. It gives me the same feeling as mulled wine does.'

I suppose she means it makes her soft and giggly because that's what she is afterwards. She doesn't go to sleep though. She encourages all of us to go into the sea.

Len doesn't really swim much but he is always diving under the water, disappearing and popping up a few yards away. We all show off to each other, doing handstands and trying to dive off each others' knees. Mum has difficulty climbing up, one foot on my knee and one on Len's. James tries to push her from behind.

'Is it the waves or the glasses of wine that are making her wobble,' he says.

She is laughing so much I think she will choke, but Len is always watching her, taking care of her. I jump over a wave. Mum catches it after me, but she dives through and under it. When she comes up, the top of her swimsuit has slipped off. I am a bit embarrassed and expect her to be too. But she just laughs and unhooks it. She says, 'Everyone else round here is topless, so why not me?' I get used to it after a while, and stop looking, and feeling a bit strange.

I think Len feels a bit strange one evening. We are getting ready to go out and eat. Mum has said she will come swimming with us in the dark before our meal, but in the end we go on our own.

'On our own Mum?' says James.

'Yes, you'll be fine. Just be careful. Look after your brother. We'll come down in half an hour and take you to the restaurant.'

I want to ask questions but it doesn't seem right to do that. We collect our things. Len says nothing. I think he has been crying. It worries me all the way to the sea.

'Why was Len upset, James?' I ask.

'He probably just wanted Mum to himself for a bit, don't worry.'

Swimming in the dark is fun. You can't see what's under the water.

'Stay close,' says James, 'don't go out too far.'

'I know something is up because Mum wouldn't let us go swimming on our own in the day time, let alone in the evening,' I say to James.

'Oh Mum knows this is a really safe bay, and we are sensible.'

James is acting all grown-up and soon calls me out of the water and makes me get dressed. While we are waiting we talk about Len.

'Do you remember on the boat how for a while he was different, quiet. I couldn't speak to him, didn't know what to talk about,' I say.

James replies with something clever like, 'Sometimes there are spaces in Len's life like empty pockets in a poacher's jacket, not spoken of, but there anyway'.

'Yes,' I say. I don't really know what he means. Except that sometimes I feel spaces, like now for instance, when we are sent off on our own, and I feel things are not quite right. I shiver.

'Are you cold?' asks James.

He makes me jump up and down with him, swinging our arms over our heads. Suddenly we hear running footsteps and Len's voice.

'Slow down. They're fine. I can see them.' Then Mum is hugging us so tight, she takes our breath away. 'Sorry, sorry,' she keeps repeating. I am not sure what she is sorry for. Len puts his arm round me to warm me, and he and Mum link James.

'Let's go for a luscious pizza. I'm starving,' says Len.

'So am I,' says James, 'I want melted cheese and garlic sausage and olives.'

'And wine, wine, wine,' says Mum, smiling. Is that a tear halfway down her cheek? She brushes it quickly away.

We go to eat pizzas, and everyone's happy and warm, and our ice-creams have sparklers stuck in them.

I have come here today to hear how he died. I sit at the back of this courtroom. It is heavy with dark panelled wood and a sense of sadness. I listen to what they have to say. At first it seems they are talking of something that is no concern of mine.

'Traces of distalgesic in the bone marrow.'

'How much?'

'Just as much as you would take for a headache.'

'So not the cause of death?'

'Well, we have to think, would there have been anything left after all this time, if he hadn't taken an enormous amount?'

'So you cannot say for certain?'

'No.'

The doctor and coroner are chatting over something I cannot visualize, nor do I want to. Then it is the turn of the man who carried out the autopsy. What would be his title, I wonder?

'The teeth tell me . . . '

What is this? What are these words? I am here to learn how he died, and they are naming bits and pieces, traces of this and that. My husband is strong, muscular, a man, and I am that man's wife. We are real people. Yet they do not seem to recognize this fact, do not care that I am sitting in this place, hearing every word.

'He was covered in black plastic bags.'

'And what does this say to you?' The coroner leans towards the doctor, almost conspiratorially.

'I am sure they were just for protection from the intense cold. The arms of this man were folded and the air could freely circulate.'

'So you rule out suffocation?'

'Well, of course we cannot be sure, after all this time.'

I begin to tremble, my ears are full of rushing water. I shake myself. I need to hear, though I may not believe.

'There was a bottle by his side.'

'Alcohol?'

'No, not alcohol – a soft drink and also foil from the distalgesic.'

So why did he die? I want to shout out, but my mouth is dry and my tongue seems to be twice its size. An empty bottle at his side but not alcohol. Evidence of distalgesic, yet not that much. Covered in plastic bags, yet with enough space to breathe. My mind blots out again the detail of what was found. So, tell me why he died and how. And yet they cannot in the end.

In the edge of the forest in a soft, pine-needled ditch, did he choose to take his life or was he just resting away from everything? He could not have meant to die. He would have left me a note, told me how much he loved me, asked my forgiveness. I have searched everywhere for that note and there is none. I have gone through all the pages of the many books, taken the backs off pictures, looked under, behind, over and in everything. There is no note. I do not believe he meant to die.

The doctor is talking again. 'He was suffering from depression, of course. We discovered he had been admitted to hospital at one time. He was diagnosed manic-depressive. He was only in hospital two weeks.'

Yes, I remember he told me that he was in hospital for a while. His occupational therapy was to make coffins out of matchsticks to award people who completed the Lyke Wake Walk. What a mindless occupation, surely this would make a person's mental health deteriorate. The Lyke Wake Walk is in North Yorkshire They used to carry the dead in their coffins this way, across the hills for burial, or so they say. I don't understand about manic-depression. I had not known that Len was labelled this until the police informed me during their investigations. I dismissed it. He was only in hospital two weeks, it couldn't have been serious. Sometimes I am so naïve.

'He may have been confused.' The doctor is talking. 'He was suffering from pains in his neck and head from the strain he was under.'

'He could in fact, just have had a heart attack,' the coroner says brightly, and laughs. Yes, laughs.

'Oh my God,' I sob, and only then do they realize, or perhaps register, that they are talking of a much-loved man, and that I am sitting here, the one who loves him.

'If he was confused,' the doctor goes on, in a more subdued voice, 'and if he lay down and slept, in those temperatures he would have died from hypothermia anyway.'

'So?' I hear myself say loudly.

'Tell me what happened, tell me how he died.' I whisper this.

Then I am still, hushed, knowing they can tell me no more than I already know. There is no answer. They do not really know how he died. Do they really know who he is?

'I must then record an open verdict,' says the coroner finally, and he writes something on a paper in front of him.

Open, for the rest of my life, to contemplate upon, to wonder and to weep over.

Afterwards they shake my hand and offer sympathy and I go away, thinking perhaps it was not him after all, and I should continue my search.

I have a new black dress to wear. Len loved to see me dressed in black. It's nearly three months now since Len was found. A Scottish couple. The police gave me their names and addresses. I should write to them but what would I say? 'Thank you for finding him, how awful for you.' ? I cannot think of suitable words – there are none perhaps. So I do not write.

I climb into the funeral car. Everything is black around me, or is it just my eyes that see everything black. But no, we drive slowly past a neighbour's house. There is a Christmas tree in the bay window. The fairy lights are switched on bright and colourful and ahead of me, in the leading car, I can see a wreath of deep red roses, a mark of love from me.

The man from the corner walks his dog. He bows his head as we move slowly out of our side street onto the main road. Round me in the car, like a shield of protection, sit my children, hardly children now, more young men and young woman.

Michael comforts Len's mother who is frail and resigned to it all.

'I've done my crying. I'm cried out,' she says stubbornly, her mouth trembling. She seems glad anyway of Michael's hand to steady her as we arrive at the crematorium chapel. No church service. Len did not really believe, he said, except, 'It's something in ourselves, the spirituality is in us.'

I, who think of myself as a Christian, had to agree with him. Nevertheless in spite of his views, we are having a small service in the chapel, to comfort us who are left behind. My children's faces are white and anxious. I hate to see them sad yet again.

The priest waits at the door. He is a friend of mine. I am glad it is him. His cassock blows in the sudden breeze. He comes to offer me sympathy, hold me for a moment.

Men in long black coats take the coffin from the car and swing it easily on to their shoulders. In Lebanon I have seen them bounce the coffin in the air as though there is nothing inside. This is to fool any evil presence that may snatch away a strong well-built young person. I stop my mind from thinking of what is inside this wooden box. I close off my thoughts as I have learnt to do over the weeks since he was found. I remember instead a wood and banks of bluebells. Len and I sat amongst them breathing in their scent. I wish they could have covered this box in place of the red roses.

My mind fights the unreality of everything again. The doubt that it is really him floods back in. The impatience to get on with the search returns. His mother is crying now and the sick hopelessness is with me again.

The priest's voice booms out, 'This sorrow must end.'

And I want to shout, 'No!' I need to feel this sorrow, this pain, it is all I have left of him. It is the part of my love for him that I can physically feel. Let me keep that forever.

The curtains are closing.

A friend of ours plays guitar. Soft folk music that Len loved. I have not had time to get to know Len's children properly. Yet we weep together. I place his chain and pendant into his daughter's hand.

And now Christmas is upon us. We have planned to be together, all of us, but it is only one week after the funeral. Is now the time to mourn? The tangled wilderness that was once my brain struggles to find an answer. Have I mourned already? There was an abundance of tears. That wasn't done in the belief that he was gone forever, it was done in the hope that he would return. And do I believe now, that he is gone forever?

How long must we go on with sad faces, sackcloth and ashes?

I will mourn forever perhaps, but my family . . . ?

I remember some of the readings from Ecclesiastes, so powerful in the chapel.
I find my rather neglected bible and read,
*There is a time for everything*
*A time to be born and a time to die,*
*. . . a time to heal*
*. . . a time to weep and a time to laugh*
*. . . a time to mourn and a time to dance*
*. . . a time to search and a time to give up'*
admittedly the latter will be harder for me, but, further down,
*'. . . know that there is nothing better for people than to be happy and do good while they live.'*

I decide to 'do good' by my family. They shall not have Christmas abandoned, just to be marked by a mournful trip to church. They will celebrate, and that is what the priest said a funeral is all about, a celebration of someone's life. We will blend the celebrations of Len's life and Christmas together.

We do. We laugh, we play games, we heal a little, we dance, we eat and drink and we sing joyful carols in the church on Christmas Eve. We do not feel guilty. Well, perhaps I do, just a little, now and then.

On Christmas night when all is quiet, I look from my window into a clear night. Even the yellow street lights cannot outshine the many brilliant stars that I can see above. I allow myself some sadness for a while. If only I could have had some sign from you, Len, so that all this is plausible to me, not some complex dream.

Now, unexpectedly, a shooting star drops slowly across the sky, so perfect, so radiant, as though it has been thrown deliberately, and just for me.

I know what I know. I believe what I believe. I do not have to explain the stars to anyone but me.


The most difficult part about life now is, I still cannot let go. I have experienced identifying belongings, attending a funeral, yet I still expect to find him, still believe he will walk through the door, or stop face to face with me in the street. I won't let go. I go on searching.

I talk to myself logically, setting the facts out, but then I argue with myself. He has a brilliant mind. If he wanted to take on someone else's identity I know he could do it. Whatever they found in the forest could have been anyone, a similar but dead person.

There was an open verdict on *how* he died, I don't believe they could absolutely, positively identify *who* it was either. A few belongings don't make the man. What else did they have? The shutter clicks into place in my head as it always does at this stage. In twenty years time, thirty even, will I still be expecting that, one wonderful, unforgettable day, when perhaps, just for a few minutes he is not on my mind, he will appear, resurrected from these awful conclusions other people have come to?


This day has been hanging over me like a suspended bolt of lightning for weeks now. We congregate outside the building, hoping to draw support from each other. The results are inside on the notice board, announcing our success, or failure, and we walk nervously in through the entrance. I find my name easily on the list. It is where I expected it to be – a good average – a 2.2. I try not to be disappointed. I have had this little dream that maybe they would give me a 2.1, taking into consideration my circumstances. Foolish woman. The bolt of lightning is a bit of a damp squib really. I congratulate Jan who has a First. They go to phone partners and husbands, and I wait. We are going to celebrate in the pub. I would like to go home.

Strange really, we've been in here sipping our drinks for a while now and there's a heavy, quiet atmosphere.

'This is crazy,' says someone, 'I thought we'd all be dancing on the tables.'

Then I realize it isn't just I who feels this awful anti-climax, but all of us.

'Someone warned me this might happen,' says another voice.

'I'm going home,' says someone else.

I relax. I feel more cheerful now.

'We're all meeting up for the final party aren't we? I'm drinking this, then I'll see you there.'

We all follow suit. I walk home breathing in now and then and letting go as though I am expelling all the deadlines, the birth pangs of essay writing, and the struggle to keep awake over a particularly uninteresting piece of reading. I will miss it though. It will leave a gap. I can write BA Hons. after my name now. I go home and write to my brother and sister.

We do dance on the tables of course, at least I and a lively young man do. The wine flows and the celebrations are just as crazy as they should be. He and I share a slice of melon biting into it together cheek to cheek, juice and pips running down our chins, and caught on camera so we can share the moment with others ever after. I have forgotten that I am nearly fifty.

The caretaker comes in eventually, turning off music, switching off lights. People start to leave through the swing doors. I am reluctant to go, and hang back, one of the last. The young man has gone already. I put on my coat, go towards the swing doors which have closed again, but before I can go through I find myself firmly clasped in someone's arms and soundly and beautifully kissed. A lecturer I hardly know.

'Too much wine,' I stammer, and run to catch the others.

I suppose being on my own without a partner for many years of my life means there have been more opportunities to meet an assortment of men. After all, my first marriage only lasted thirteen years and my marriage to Len only sixteen short months. Yes, over the years there have been men in my life. I think of various encounters more as skirmishes than serious relationships. I never feel I need a man, never go looking 'all around the orchard', never really take any of them seriously. As soon as a man talks about marriage or wants to share my bed permanently, up go the barriers. I suppose a psychiatrist might say I have a problem, might deduce that I don't trust men, have a fear of being let down. I have been let down. On the other hand I have had fun, enjoyed many occasions with people of the opposite sex.

I have probably become too independent. I like to be able to choose what I want to do when I wake up in the morning. I am perhaps a little selfish now. I want to be all that I can be. Relationships might interfere with this. There have been no serious involvements over the last few years apart from Len, but many deep and lasting friendships. I think I prefer that.

'Be brave Mum, you know you can be.' James is home from University. They are all here for my graduation day.

'I get my courage from all of you,' I say, 'and I'm going to need it if I have to get up on that stage today.'

'There are two tickets allotted to each family for the ceremony,' I am told. But somehow I have obtained eight, and others who are eager to see my 'moment of glory', walk through without one.

I go with other students to find the cap and gowns we have hired. We have a few comic moments learning how to wear these weird garments, then we emerge into the street to walk to the City Hall. The street is full of black-gowned students, many with the gold and blue colours that adorn my gown. Like birds of paradise we strut and billow our way towards the Hall, to say a few final words to family and friends before taking our places.

Cameras are clicking now and the tassel on my hat is dealt with.

'Mum keep the tassel at the side, if you keep looking at it that way, you'll look cross-eyed in all the photos.'

Lots of pictures are taken. Posing on my own, with friend Jan, with sister Elsie and nephew, trying to take the whole thing seriously but failing now and then, in the excitement and relief that it is all over and I have done it.

Finally the picture of myself and my four children. We are so proud of each other.

Now quietly we line up. It is time to go and shake the hand, receive the scroll, and for a moment I am saddened by the thought that three people who would have been here, prouder of me than almost any others, are missing from this ceremony. Len, my father, and my dear mother who so recently died. I visualize the little rusted lozenge tin that I found among her things, containing sequins that were never sewn upon our ballet dresses, some of them still shining like jewels after all that time.

It's almost my turn now and I say a little prayer that I will not trip, will not drop my hat. Now my section is announced.

'Instead of clapping every student, for time is short, please just clap at the end of each set of students,' we are instructed.

I am near the beginning of this line-up as my name begins with A, about fourth or fifth.

My heart is pumping away and I am walking up the steps, on to the stage. My name is announced and in the quiet I start the long walk across to Lord Short. Suddenly I am convinced that if I look into this sea of faces I will see that one face that I am so afraid is beginning to fade from my mind, the face I thought would be fixed in my memory forever. I hesitate just for a moment and glance down. The hall is in darkness and it is difficult to see anyone, but I see his face more clearly than I have ever seen it over the past year. I am filled with a sense of relief somehow. I walk on.

A sudden clapping begins and I know it is my children who cannot contain themselves. There is cheering and stamping of feet as several others join them.

My face is getting hotter and I am trying so hard not to laugh out loud.

'You have a lot of fans,' says Lord Short.

'It's my children, I never could control them.'

I take the scroll from him, shake the hand offered to me, look towards my lovely family, bow, and go on my way. And the three sequins that I have stitched to the hem of my dress flash in the spotlight, and I feel like a butterfly.

*In my search, I camp high up there on Simonside. It is spring. The nights are so cold. A million stars form a dome above me. Their beauty increases the terrible ache inside me. I sleep with my head outside the tent. I want to be near to him somehow.*

*I am woken by a barn owl. It sits upon the fence, illuminated by the moon. I listen to its soft call. My hair is stiff and frosted. I think it might shatter like spun glass.*

*The days are so hot. The skies deep blue. Once we would have walked together, striding out, breathing in the pure air, our lungs feeling as though they had soaked up laughing gas. Now I put one foot in front of the other, pushing myself slowly up the hillside, testing my intuition, hoping my head or heart can pinpoint his place.*

*I would cover him with leaves. Never tell anyone where he chose to sleep.*

*Instead I sit beneath a twisted hawthorn tree looking at the view. We plant roses here. They die. Amongst the heather we spread ashes. Strange, I didn't think that they would be like this, orange and purple. The breeze up here blows some of them back onto me. In my confusion, I do not know if I should shake them off, or leave them tangled in my hair.*